Math 87
Test Masters

Section 1

Test A—100 Addition Facts

Name _____ Time _____

3 + 2 = 5	8 + 3 = 11	2 + 1 = 3	5 + 6 = 11	2 + 9 = 11	4 + 8 = 12	8 + 0 = 8	3 + 9 = 12	1 + 0 = 1	6 + 3 = 9
7 + 3 = 10	1 + 6 = 7	4 + 7 = 11	0 + 3 = 3	6 + 4 = 10	5 + 5 = 10	3 + 1 = 4	7 + 2 = 9	8 + 5 = 13	2 + 5 = 7
4 + 0 = 4	5 + 7 = 12	1 + 1 = 2	5 + 4 = 9	2 + 8 = 10	7 + 1 = 8	4 + 6 = 10	0 + 2 = 2	6 + 5 = 11	4 + 9 = 13
8 + 6 = 14	0 + 4 = 4	5 + 8 = 13	7 + 4 = 11	1 + 7 = 8	6 + 6 = 12	4 + 1 = 5	8 + 2 = 10	2 + 4 = 6	6 + 0 = 6
9 + 1 = 10	8 + 8 = 16	2 + 2 = 4	4 + 5 = 9	6 + 2 = 8	0 + 0 = 0	5 + 9 = 14	3 + 3 = 6	8 + 1 = 9	2 + 7 = 9
4 + 4 = 8	7 + 5 = 12	0 + 1 = 1	8 + 7 = 15	3 + 4 = 7	7 + 9 = 16	1 + 2 = 3	6 + 7 = 13	0 + 8 = 8	9 + 2 = 11
0 + 9 = 9	8 + 9 = 17	7 + 6 = 13	1 + 3 = 4	6 + 8 = 14	2 + 0 = 2	8 + 4 = 12	3 + 5 = 8	9 + 8 = 17	5 + 0 = 5
9 + 3 = 12	2 + 6 = 8	3 + 0 = 3	6 + 1 = 7	3 + 6 = 9	5 + 2 = 7	0 + 5 = 5	6 + 9 = 15	1 + 8 = 9	9 + 6 = 15
4 + 3 = 7	9 + 9 = 18	0 + 7 = 7	9 + 4 = 13	7 + 7 = 14	1 + 4 = 5	3 + 7 = 10	7 + 0 = 7	2 + 3 = 5	5 + 1 = 6
9 + 5 = 14	1 + 5 = 6	9 + 0 = 9	3 + 8 = 11	1 + 9 = 10	5 + 3 = 8	4 + 2 = 6	9 + 7 = 16	0 + 6 = 6	7 + 8 = 15

MATH 87 by Hake and Saxon

1

16 − 9 **7**	7 − 1 **6**	18 − 9 **9**	11 − 3 **8**	13 − 7 **6**	8 − 2 **6**	11 − 5 **6**	5 − 0 **5**	17 − 9 **8**	6 − 1 **5**
10 − 9 **1**	6 − 2 **4**	13 − 4 **9**	4 − 0 **4**	10 − 5 **5**	5 − 1 **4**	10 − 3 **7**	12 − 6 **6**	10 − 1 **9**	6 − 4 **2**
7 − 2 **5**	14 − 7 **7**	8 − 1 **7**	11 − 6 **5**	3 − 3 **0**	16 − 7 **9**	5 − 2 **3**	12 − 4 **8**	3 − 0 **3**	11 − 7 **4**
17 − 8 **9**	6 − 0 **6**	10 − 6 **4**	4 − 1 **3**	9 − 5 **4**	9 − 0 **9**	5 − 4 **1**	12 − 5 **7**	4 − 2 **2**	9 − 3 **6**
12 − 3 **9**	16 − 8 **8**	9 − 1 **8**	15 − 6 **9**	11 − 4 **7**	13 − 5 **8**	1 − 0 **1**	8 − 5 **3**	9 − 6 **3**	11 − 2 **9**
7 − 0 **7**	10 − 8 **2**	6 − 3 **3**	14 − 5 **9**	3 − 1 **2**	8 − 6 **2**	4 − 4 **0**	11 − 8 **3**	3 − 2 **1**	15 − 9 **6**
13 − 8 **5**	7 − 4 **3**	10 − 7 **3**	0 − 0 **0**	12 − 8 **4**	5 − 5 **0**	4 − 3 **1**	8 − 7 **1**	7 − 3 **4**	7 − 6 **1**
5 − 3 **2**	7 − 5 **2**	2 − 1 **1**	6 − 6 **0**	8 − 4 **4**	2 − 2 **0**	13 − 6 **7**	15 − 8 **7**	2 − 0 **2**	13 − 9 **4**
1 − 1 **0**	11 − 9 **2**	10 − 4 **6**	9 − 2 **7**	14 − 6 **8**	8 − 0 **8**	9 − 4 **5**	10 − 2 **8**	6 − 5 **1**	8 − 3 **5**
7 − 7 **0**	14 − 8 **6**	12 − 9 **3**	9 − 8 **1**	12 − 7 **5**	9 − 9 **0**	15 − 7 **8**	8 − 8 **0**	14 − 9 **5**	9 − 7 **2**

9 ×9 **81**	3 ×5 **15**	8 ×5 **40**	2 ×6 **12**	4 ×7 **28**	0 ×3 **0**	7 ×2 **14**	1 ×5 **5**	7 ×8 **56**	4 ×0 **0**
3 ×4 **12**	5 ×9 **45**	0 ×2 **0**	7 ×3 **21**	4 ×1 **4**	2 ×7 **14**	6 ×3 **18**	5 ×4 **20**	1 ×0 **0**	9 ×2 **18**
1 ×1 **1**	9 ×0 **0**	2 ×8 **16**	6 ×4 **24**	0 ×7 **0**	8 ×1 **8**	3 ×3 **9**	4 ×8 **32**	9 ×3 **27**	2 ×0 **0**
4 ×9 **36**	7 ×0 **0**	1 ×2 **2**	8 ×4 **32**	6 ×5 **30**	2 ×9 **18**	9 ×4 **36**	0 ×1 **0**	7 ×4 **28**	5 ×8 **40**
0 ×8 **0**	4 ×2 **8**	9 ×8 **72**	3 ×6 **18**	5 ×5 **25**	1 ×6 **6**	5 ×0 **0**	6 ×6 **36**	2 ×1 **2**	7 ×9 **63**
9 ×1 **9**	2 ×2 **4**	5 ×1 **5**	4 ×3 **12**	0 ×0 **0**	8 ×9 **72**	3 ×7 **21**	9 ×7 **63**	1 ×7 **7**	6 ×0 **0**
5 ×6 **30**	7 ×5 **35**	3 ×0 **0**	8 ×8 **64**	1 ×3 **3**	8 ×3 **24**	5 ×2 **10**	0 ×4 **0**	9 ×5 **45**	6 ×7 **42**
2 ×3 **6**	8 ×6 **48**	0 ×5 **0**	6 ×1 **6**	3 ×8 **24**	7 ×6 **42**	1 ×8 **8**	9 ×6 **54**	4 ×4 **16**	5 ×3 **15**
7 ×7 **49**	1 ×4 **4**	6 ×2 **12**	4 ×5 **20**	2 ×4 **8**	8 ×0 **0**	3 ×1 **3**	6 ×8 **48**	0 ×9 **0**	8 ×7 **56**
3 ×2 **6**	4 ×6 **24**	1 ×9 **9**	5 ×7 **35**	8 ×2 **16**	0 ×6 **0**	7 ×1 **7**	2 ×5 **10**	6 ×9 **54**	3 ×9 **27**

5 × 6 30	4 × 3 12	9 × 8 72	7 × 5 35	2 × 9 18	8 × 4 32	9 × 3 27	6 × 9 54
9 × 4 36	2 × 5 10	7 × 6 42	4 × 8 32	7 × 9 63	5 × 4 20	3 × 2 6	9 × 7 63
3 × 7 21	8 × 5 40	6 × 2 12	5 × 5 25	3 × 5 15	2 × 4 8	7 × 7 49	8 × 9 72
6 × 4 24	2 × 8 16	4 × 4 16	8 × 2 16	3 × 9 27	6 × 6 36	9 × 9 81	5 × 3 15
4 × 6 24	8 × 8 64	5 × 7 35	6 × 3 18	2 × 2 4	7 × 4 28	3 × 8 24	8 × 6 48
2 × 6 12	5 × 9 45	3 × 3 9	9 × 2 18	6 × 7 42	4 × 5 20	7 × 2 14	9 × 6 54
5 × 2 10	7 × 8 56	2 × 3 6	6 × 8 48	4 × 7 28	9 × 5 45	3 × 6 18	8 × 7 56
3 × 4 12	7 × 3 21	5 × 8 40	4 × 2 8	8 × 3 24	2 × 7 14	6 × 5 30	4 × 9 36

$7\overline{)21}$	$2\overline{)10}$	$6\overline{)42}$	$1\overline{)3}$	$4\overline{)24}$	$3\overline{)6}$	$9\overline{)54}$	$6\overline{)18}$	$4\overline{)0}$	$5\overline{)30}$
$4\overline{)32}$	$8\overline{)56}$	$1\overline{)0}$	$6\overline{)12}$	$3\overline{)18}$	$9\overline{)72}$	$5\overline{)15}$	$2\overline{)8}$	$7\overline{)42}$	$6\overline{)36}$
$6\overline{)0}$	$5\overline{)10}$	$9\overline{)9}$	$2\overline{)6}$	$7\overline{)63}$	$4\overline{)16}$	$8\overline{)48}$	$1\overline{)2}$	$5\overline{)35}$	$3\overline{)21}$
$2\overline{)18}$	$6\overline{)6}$	$3\overline{)15}$	$8\overline{)40}$	$2\overline{)0}$	$5\overline{)20}$	$9\overline{)27}$	$1\overline{)8}$	$4\overline{)4}$	$7\overline{)35}$
$4\overline{)20}$	$9\overline{)63}$	$1\overline{)4}$	$7\overline{)14}$	$3\overline{)3}$	$8\overline{)24}$	$5\overline{)0}$	$6\overline{)24}$	$8\overline{)8}$	$2\overline{)16}$
$5\overline{)5}$	$8\overline{)64}$	$3\overline{)0}$	$4\overline{)28}$	$7\overline{)49}$	$2\overline{)4}$	$9\overline{)81}$	$3\overline{)12}$	$6\overline{)30}$	$1\overline{)5}$
$8\overline{)32}$	$1\overline{)1}$	$9\overline{)36}$	$3\overline{)27}$	$2\overline{)14}$	$5\overline{)25}$	$6\overline{)48}$	$8\overline{)0}$	$7\overline{)28}$	$4\overline{)36}$
$2\overline{)12}$	$5\overline{)45}$	$1\overline{)7}$	$4\overline{)8}$	$7\overline{)0}$	$8\overline{)16}$	$3\overline{)24}$	$9\overline{)45}$	$1\overline{)9}$	$6\overline{)54}$
$7\overline{)56}$	$9\overline{)0}$	$8\overline{)72}$	$2\overline{)2}$	$5\overline{)40}$	$3\overline{)9}$	$9\overline{)18}$	$1\overline{)6}$	$4\overline{)12}$	$7\overline{)7}$

$\frac{12}{5} = 2\frac{2}{5}$	$\frac{7}{2} = 3\frac{1}{2}$	$\frac{20}{3} = 6\frac{2}{3}$	$\frac{5}{2} = 2\frac{1}{2}$	$\frac{24}{12} = 2$
$\frac{10}{2} = 5$	$\frac{25}{6} = 4\frac{1}{6}$	$\frac{5}{4} = 1\frac{1}{4}$	$\frac{21}{8} = 2\frac{5}{8}$	$\frac{6}{3} = 2$
$\frac{10}{5} = 2$	$\frac{21}{10} = 2\frac{1}{10}$	$\frac{12}{12} = 1$	$\frac{15}{3} = 5$	$\frac{10}{3} = 3\frac{1}{3}$
$\frac{16}{16} = 1$	$\frac{5}{3} = 1\frac{2}{3}$	$\frac{27}{10} = 2\frac{7}{10}$	$\frac{3}{2} = 1\frac{1}{2}$	$\frac{11}{8} = 1\frac{3}{8}$
$\frac{36}{12} = 3$	$\frac{11}{10} = 1\frac{1}{10}$	$\frac{21}{16} = 1\frac{5}{16}$	$\frac{4}{4} = 1$	$\frac{25}{9} = 2\frac{7}{9}$
$\frac{11}{6} = 1\frac{5}{6}$	$\frac{8}{8} = 1$	$\frac{20}{9} = 2\frac{2}{9}$	$\frac{15}{2} = 7\frac{1}{2}$	$\frac{4}{3} = 1\frac{1}{3}$
$\frac{25}{8} = 3\frac{1}{8}$	$\frac{15}{4} = 3\frac{3}{4}$	$\frac{2}{2} = 1$	$\frac{25}{12} = 2\frac{1}{12}$	$\frac{32}{16} = 2$
$\frac{8}{3} = 2\frac{2}{3}$	$\frac{12}{4} = 3$	$\frac{25}{16} = 1\frac{9}{16}$	$\frac{8}{5} = 1\frac{3}{5}$	$\frac{27}{8} = 3\frac{3}{8}$
$\frac{33}{20} = 1\frac{13}{20}$	$\frac{4}{2} = 2$	$\frac{10}{9} = 1\frac{1}{9}$	$\frac{24}{8} = 3$	$\frac{3}{3} = 1$
$\frac{9}{4} = 2\frac{1}{4}$	$\frac{10}{10} = 1$	$\frac{15}{8} = 1\frac{7}{8}$	$\frac{16}{3} = 5\frac{1}{3}$	$\frac{33}{10} = 3\frac{3}{10}$

$\frac{4}{20} = \frac{1}{5}$	$\frac{2}{4} = \frac{1}{2}$	$\frac{4}{12} = \frac{1}{3}$	$\frac{6}{9} = \frac{2}{3}$	$\frac{4}{8} = \frac{1}{2}$
$\frac{4}{10} = \frac{2}{5}$	$\frac{2}{16} = \frac{1}{8}$	$\frac{10}{15} = \frac{2}{3}$	$\frac{2}{8} = \frac{1}{4}$	$\frac{10}{12} = \frac{5}{6}$
$\frac{8}{12} = \frac{2}{3}$	$\frac{2}{20} = \frac{1}{10}$	$\frac{2}{6} = \frac{1}{3}$	$\frac{6}{10} = \frac{3}{5}$	$\frac{12}{24} = \frac{1}{2}$
$\frac{14}{16} = \frac{7}{8}$	$\frac{6}{12} = \frac{1}{2}$	$\frac{10}{100} = \frac{1}{10}$	$\frac{3}{15} = \frac{1}{5}$	$\frac{6}{8} = \frac{3}{4}$
$\frac{3}{6} = \frac{1}{2}$	$\frac{10}{20} = \frac{1}{2}$	$\frac{3}{12} = \frac{1}{4}$	$\frac{3}{9} = \frac{1}{3}$	$\frac{4}{16} = \frac{1}{4}$
$\frac{8}{10} = \frac{4}{5}$	$\frac{16}{32} = \frac{1}{2}$	$\frac{4}{6} = \frac{2}{3}$	$\frac{8}{16} = \frac{1}{2}$	$\frac{5}{20} = \frac{1}{4}$
$\frac{50}{100} = \frac{1}{2}$	$\frac{2}{10} = \frac{1}{5}$	$\frac{5}{15} = \frac{1}{3}$	$\frac{9}{12} = \frac{3}{4}$	$\frac{10}{16} = \frac{5}{8}$
$\frac{2}{12} = \frac{1}{6}$	$\frac{12}{16} = \frac{3}{4}$	$\frac{7}{14} = \frac{1}{2}$	$\frac{5}{10} = \frac{1}{2}$	$\frac{4}{32} = \frac{1}{8}$

$\frac{12}{16} = \frac{3}{4}$	$\frac{16}{24} = \frac{2}{3}$	$\frac{20}{6} = 3\frac{1}{3}$	$\frac{6}{21} = \frac{2}{7}$	$\frac{14}{8} = 1\frac{3}{4}$
$\frac{18}{24} = \frac{3}{4}$	$\frac{15}{6} = 2\frac{1}{2}$	$\frac{6}{8} = \frac{3}{4}$	$\frac{8}{3} = 2\frac{2}{3}$	$\frac{5}{10} = \frac{1}{2}$
$\frac{25}{12} = 2\frac{1}{12}$	$\frac{24}{9} = 2\frac{2}{3}$	$\frac{16}{20} = \frac{4}{5}$	$\frac{18}{8} = 2\frac{1}{4}$	$\frac{15}{24} = \frac{5}{8}$
$\frac{8}{6} = 1\frac{1}{3}$	$\frac{9}{6} = 1\frac{1}{2}$	$\frac{10}{4} = 2\frac{1}{2}$	$\frac{25}{100} = \frac{1}{4}$	$\frac{6}{4} = 1\frac{1}{2}$
$\frac{8}{24} = \frac{1}{3}$	$\frac{10}{8} = 1\frac{1}{4}$	$\frac{20}{6} = 3\frac{1}{3}$	$\frac{20}{16} = 1\frac{1}{4}$	$\frac{15}{20} = \frac{3}{4}$
$\frac{16}{16} = 1$	$\frac{25}{10} = 2\frac{1}{2}$	$\frac{21}{6} = 3\frac{1}{2}$	$\frac{8}{12} = \frac{2}{3}$	$\frac{12}{8} = 1\frac{1}{2}$
$\frac{8}{12} = \frac{2}{3}$	$\frac{12}{9} = 1\frac{1}{3}$	$\frac{16}{32} = \frac{1}{2}$	$\frac{20}{9} = 2\frac{2}{9}$	$\frac{10}{3} = 3\frac{1}{3}$
$\frac{20}{8} = 2\frac{1}{2}$	$\frac{10}{6} = 1\frac{2}{3}$	$\frac{12}{20} = \frac{3}{5}$	$\frac{18}{12} = 1\frac{1}{2}$	$\frac{12}{10} = 1\frac{1}{5}$

$\dfrac{1}{5} = 0.2$	$\dfrac{3}{10} = 0.3$	$\dfrac{1}{4} = 0.25$	$\dfrac{1}{20} = 0.05$
$\dfrac{1}{8} = 0.125$	$\dfrac{1}{3} = 0.\overline{3}$	$\dfrac{9}{10} = 0.9$	$\dfrac{7}{8} = 0.875$
$\dfrac{3}{5} = 0.6$	$\dfrac{1}{6} = 0.1\overline{6}$	$\dfrac{1}{2} = 0.5$	$\dfrac{1}{100} = 0.01$
$\dfrac{1}{50} = 0.02$	$\dfrac{5}{8} = 0.625$	$\dfrac{7}{10} = 0.7$	$\dfrac{3}{4} = 0.75$
$\dfrac{1}{25} = 0.04$	$\dfrac{2}{3} = 0.\overline{6}$	$\dfrac{2}{5} = 0.4$	$\dfrac{5}{6} = 0.8\overline{3}$
$\dfrac{3}{8} = 0.375$	$\dfrac{4}{5} = 0.8$	$\dfrac{1}{10} = 0.1$	$\dfrac{1}{1000} = 0.001$

$1\% = \dfrac{1}{100}$	$20\% = \dfrac{1}{5}$	$55\% = \dfrac{11}{20}$	$90\% = \dfrac{9}{10}$	$75\% = \dfrac{3}{4}$
$99\% = \dfrac{99}{100}$	$5\% = \dfrac{1}{20}$	$95\% = \dfrac{19}{20}$	$80\% = \dfrac{4}{5}$	$12\% = \dfrac{3}{25}$
$70\% = \dfrac{7}{10}$	$65\% = \dfrac{13}{20}$	$50\% = \dfrac{1}{2}$	$2\% = \dfrac{1}{50}$	$48\% = \dfrac{12}{25}$
$24\% = \dfrac{6}{25}$	$25\% = \dfrac{1}{4}$	$33\tfrac{1}{3}\% = \dfrac{1}{3}$	$40\% = \dfrac{2}{5}$	$15\% = \dfrac{3}{20}$
$60\% = \dfrac{3}{5}$	$30\% = \dfrac{3}{10}$	$4\% = \dfrac{1}{25}$	$35\% = \dfrac{7}{20}$	$36\% = \dfrac{9}{25}$
$45\% = \dfrac{9}{20}$	$8\% = \dfrac{2}{25}$	$10\% = \dfrac{1}{10}$	$66\tfrac{2}{3}\% = \dfrac{2}{3}$	$85\% = \dfrac{17}{20}$

Fraction	Decimal	Percent
$\frac{1}{100}$	0.01	1%
$\frac{1}{50}$	0.02	2%
$\frac{1}{4}$	0.25	25%
$\frac{1}{8}$	0.125	12.5%
$\frac{1}{20}$	0.05	5%
$\frac{1}{3}$	$0.\overline{3}$	$33.\overline{3}$%
$\frac{7}{10}$	0.7	70%
$\frac{2}{5}$	0.4	40%
$\frac{1}{6}$	$0.1\overline{6}$	$16.\overline{6}$%
$\frac{3}{8}$	0.375	37.5%
$\frac{1}{2}$	0.5	50%
$\frac{1}{10}$	0.1	10%
$\frac{1}{5}$	0.2	20%
$\frac{1}{1000}$	0.001	0.1%
$\frac{1}{12}$	$0.08\overline{3}$	$8.\overline{3}$%
$\frac{2}{3}$	$0.\overline{6}$	$66.\overline{6}$%
$\frac{5}{8}$	0.625	62.5%
$\frac{4}{5}$	0.8	80%
$\frac{5}{6}$	$0.8\overline{3}$	$83.\overline{3}$%
$\frac{3}{10}$	0.3	30%
$\frac{3}{4}$	0.75	75%
$\frac{7}{8}$	0.875	87.5%
$\frac{9}{10}$	0.9	90%
$\frac{3}{5}$	0.6	60%
$\frac{1}{25}$	0.04	4%

TEST 1 FORM A

1. 10
2. 1, 2, 5, 10, 25, 50
3. −7 < 2
4. Twenty-one million, six hundred thousand, fifty
5. 1
6. 1, 2, 3, 4, 5, 6, 7, 10
7. >
8.

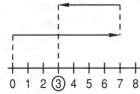

0 1 ②3 4 5 6 7 8 9

9. 8,100,060
10. $10.70
11. 15,160
12. $9.25
13. 1348
14. 35
15. 23,440
16. 1056
17. 519
18. 5799
19. 2720
20. $2.98

TEST 1 FORM B

1. 12
2. 1, 2, 4, 5, 8, 10, 20, 40
3. −3 < 2
4. Thirty-one million, twenty thousand, thirty
5. 1
6. 1, 2, 4, 5, 7, 10
7. >
8.

0 1 2 ③4 5 6 7 8

9. 12,300,040
10. $11.60
11. 12,870

---

12. $7.10
13. 22
14. 2146
15. 2414
16. 1080
17. 447
18. 5145 r 1
19. 2400
20. $7.65

TEST 2 FORM A

1. 227,000 visitors
2. $101.82
3. 5480 participants
4. 3799 leaves
5. $-3, 0, \frac{1}{3}, 3$
6.

7. (a) $\frac{7}{12}$ (b) $\frac{5}{12}$
8. forty-two million
9. (a) 1, 3, 7, 21
   (b) 1, 2, 3, 4, 6, 8, 12, 16, 24, 48
   (c) 1, 3
10. $1 \times 3 < 1 + 3$
11. 2440
12. $18.30
13. 26
14. $\frac{4}{5}$
15. $\frac{6}{11}$
16. $\frac{12}{35}$
17. 8256 r 5
18. $65.20
19. $\frac{8}{125}$
20. (a) ray; $\overrightarrow{MC}$
    (b) line; $\overleftrightarrow{PM}$ or $\overleftrightarrow{MP}$
    (c) segment; $\overline{FH}$ or $\overline{HF}$

TEST 2 FORM B

1. 213,000 visitors
2. $92.56
3. 4191 participants
4. 3879 leaves
5. $-2, 0, \frac{1}{2}, 2$
6.

7. (a) $\frac{5}{9}$ (b) $\frac{4}{9}$
8. fifty-three million
9. (a) 1, 3, 9, 27
   (b) 1, 3, 5, 9, 15, 45
   (c) 1, 3, 9
10. $2 \times 3 > 2 + 3$
11. 814
12. $17.35
13. 24
14. $\frac{5}{7}$
15. $\frac{4}{9}$
16. $\frac{6}{35}$
17. 9250
18. $70
19. $\frac{9}{40}$
20. (a) segment; $\overline{AB}$ or $\overline{BA}$
    (b) line; $\overleftrightarrow{CD}$ or $\overleftrightarrow{DC}$
    (c) ray; $\overrightarrow{GH}$

TEST 3 FORM A

1. 4007
2. 1200 beach balls
3. 47
4. $9.20
5. 26 years
6. 75¢ per cup; $0.75 per cup

---

7.  =

8. (a) 9 (b) 8

9. eight hundred sixty million, nine hundred thousand, three hundred thirty

10. (a) 1, 3, 7, 21
    (b) 1, 2, 3, 6, 7, 14, 21, 42
    (c) 21

11. $\overline{BC}, \overline{AB}, \overline{AC}$

12. $1\frac{6}{7}$

13. $1\frac{1}{11}$

14. $1\frac{1}{6}$

15. 2201 r 2

16. 221

17. 10,290

18. 39

19. 300

20. $11.57

Test 3 Form B

1. 3768
2. 900 beach balls
3. 29
4. $8.60
5. 13 years
6. 45¢ per lb; $0.45 per lb
7.  =

8. (a) 10 (b) 6

9. six hundred nine million, three thousand, three hundred eight

10. (a) 1, 3, 5, 15
    (b) 1, 2, 3, 5, 6, 10, 15, 30
    (c) 15

11. $\overline{XY}, \overline{YZ}, \overline{XZ}$

12. $4\frac{4}{5}$

13. $1\frac{1}{7}$

14. $1\frac{3}{8}$

15. 2004

16. 296

17. 8890

18. 44

19. 375

20. $15.17

Test 4 Form A

1. 1908
2. 160 bushels
3. $\frac{11}{12}$
4. 529 ducks
5. nine hundred fifty-three million
6. two hundred seventy-eight billion, three hundred four million, eleven thousand, fifty
7. $7 - 9 = -2$
8. 28 cm
9. (a) $3\frac{2}{3}$ (b) $\frac{3}{7}$
10. $2\frac{2}{3}$
11. (a) 27 (b) 16
12. right angle
13. 6768
14. $1.37
15. A
16. $2\frac{1}{4}$
17. $\frac{2}{11}$
18. $\frac{1}{2}$
19. 7210 r 3
20. 312

Test 4 Form B

1. 1907
2. 140 bushels
3. $\frac{7}{8}$
4. 547 ducks
5. nine hundred twenty-six million
6. eight billion, three hundred four million, eleven thousand, fifty
7. $7 - 10 = -3$
8. 24 cm
9. (a) $5\frac{3}{4}$ (b) $\frac{4}{7}$
10. $3\frac{1}{3}$
11. (a) 30 (b) 20
12. right angle
13. 2628
14. $1.34
15. C
16. $1\frac{4}{5}$
17. $\frac{1}{5}$
18. $\frac{2}{3}$
19. 6209
20. 288

Test 5 Form A

1. 675 students
2. 128 envelopes
3. one billion, six hundred forty-eight million
4. 838 stamps
5. (a) 120 spectators
   (b) 80 spectators

200 spectators	
$\frac{3}{5}$ roared with laughter	40 spectators
	40 spectators
	40 spectators
$\frac{2}{5}$ were mildly amused	40 spectators
	40 spectators

6. $3\frac{2}{3}$

7. $\frac{14}{3}$

8. $2 \cdot 2 \cdot 2 \cdot 2 \cdot 2 \cdot 3 \cdot 5$

9. (a) $\frac{10}{60}$ (b) $\frac{24}{60}$

10. side AD

11. 80 mm

12. 66

13. 83

14. 23

15. 13

16. $2\frac{1}{4}$

17. $\frac{1}{6}$

18. 12

19. $204

20. 375

TEST 5 FORM B

1. 466 students

2. 48 rolls

3. one billion, six hundred thirty-eight million

4. 27,800

5. (a) 150 spectators
   (b) 100 spectators

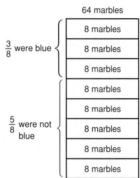

6. $3\frac{1}{2}$

7. $\frac{16}{3}$

8. $2 \cdot 5 \cdot 7 \cdot 7$

9. (a) $\frac{15}{60}$ (b) $\frac{48}{60}$

10. side AB

11. 70 mm

12. 93

13. 82

14. 32

15. 16

16. $1\frac{4}{5}$

17. $\frac{2}{5}$

18. 6

19. $153

20. 75

TEST 6 FORM A

1. 24 books

2. 844 years

3. $10.70

4. 126 pages

5. (a) 24 marbles
   (b) 40 marbles

6. (a) $\frac{7}{100}$ (b) $\frac{93}{100}$

7. (a) $13\frac{1}{2}$ (b) $9\frac{1}{3}$
   (c) $\frac{2}{15}$

8. (a) $\frac{9}{4}$ (b) $\frac{4}{27}$ (c) $\frac{1}{9}$

9. (a) 30 (b) 21

10. 350

11. 73

12. 22

13. $5\frac{1}{6}$

14. $12\frac{2}{5}$

15. $3\frac{1}{4}$

16. 8

17. $\frac{5}{6}$

18. $10\frac{2}{3}$

19. $\frac{1}{3}$

20. $\frac{11}{12}$

TEST 6 FORM B

1. 26 books

2. 645 years

3. $12.70

4. 86 pages

5. (a) 16 marbles
   (b) 48 marbles

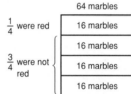

6. (a) $\frac{9}{100}$ (b) $\frac{91}{100}$

7. (a) $7\frac{1}{3}$ (b) $6\frac{2}{3}$ (c) $\frac{11}{15}$

8. (a) $\frac{8}{5}$ (b) $\frac{5}{18}$ (c) $\frac{1}{3}$

9. (a) 15 (b) 10

10. 350

11. 71

12. 23

13. $4\frac{5}{6}$

14. $9\frac{3}{5}$

15. $1\frac{3}{4}$

16. 6

17. $\frac{4}{5}$

18. $6\frac{3}{4}$

19. $\frac{1}{2}$

20. $\frac{3}{4}$

TEST 7 FORM A

1. 74 inches
2. $3.44
3. 1915 miles
4. 157 girls
5. (a) 620 miles
   (b) 1550 miles

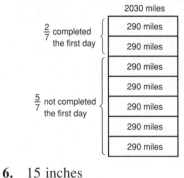

6. 9 inches
7. $\frac{8}{20}, \frac{15}{20}$
8. (a) 44,000   (b) 44,300
9. 1000
10. $4\frac{1}{2}$
11. <
12. 24
13. 5 · 43
14. 15
15. 12
16. 236
17. 49
18. $\frac{7}{12}$
19. $\frac{1}{12}$
20. $\frac{16}{25}$

TEST 7 FORM B

1. 75 inches
2. $4.54
3. 1472 miles
4. 123 boys

5. (a) 580 miles
   (b) 1450 miles

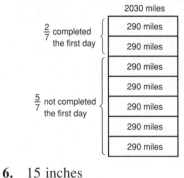

6. 15 inches
7. $\frac{12}{20}, \frac{5}{20}$
8. (a) 43,000   (b) 42,800
9. 1000
10. $2\frac{1}{4}$
11. <
12. 60
13. 2 · 2 · 5 · 11
14. 16
15. 10
16. 137
17. 39
18. $\frac{5}{12}$
19. 0
20. $1\frac{9}{16}$

TEST 8 FORM A

1. $117.43
2. $2603
3. $0.65
4. 61 seconds
5. 20 cm

6. (a) 28 fish   (b) 35 fish

7. 63
8. (a) 3849.42   (b) 3800
9. (a) $\frac{89}{100}$ (b) 0.89
10. one hundred and one hundred thirteen thousandths
11. 0.00085
12. 0.34
13. $10\frac{1}{12}$
14. 14.5
15. 5
16. 196
17. 17.09
18. 39.515
19. $1\frac{1}{10}$
20. $4\frac{3}{10}$

TEST 8 FORM B

1. $112.43
2. $298
3. $0.71
4. 62 seconds
5. 12 cm

Math 87 by Hake & Saxon

6. (a) 36 fish   (b) 27 fish

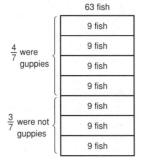

7. 126

8. (a) 3849.4   (b) 3850

9. (a) $\dfrac{11}{100}$ (b) 0.11

10. one hundred and thirteen hundredths

11. 0.00058

12. 0.57

13. $10\dfrac{1}{3}$

14. 16.5

15. 5

16. 295

17. 17.18

18. 18.537

19. $1\dfrac{1}{4}$

20. $\dfrac{11}{38}$

TEST 9 FORM A

1. $\dfrac{4}{9}$

2. (a) 340 seconds
    (b) 85 seconds

3. 441 miles

4. (a) 26 adults
    (b) 78 adults

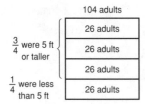

5. 310 mm

6. 30 mm

7. 4.5 cm

8. 0.910

9. seventeen and seven hundred three ten-thousandths

10. 4,250,860,000

11. 0.83

12. (a) 65.03   (b) $65\dfrac{3}{100}$

13. (a) $\angle c$ (b) $\angle e$

14. 0.0072

15. $8\dfrac{3}{14}$

16. $1\dfrac{1}{2}$

17. $13\dfrac{1}{2}$

18. $\dfrac{7}{9}$

19. 12

20. 0.82

TEST 9 FORM B

1. $\dfrac{3}{8}$

2. (a) 380 seconds
    (b) 95 seconds

3. 432 miles

4. (a) 21 adults
    (b) 84 adults

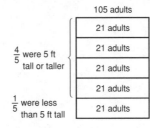

5. 300 mm

6. 40 mm

7. 2.5 cm

8. 0.910

9. thirty-seven and seven hundred one ten-thousandths

10. 2,230,586,000

11. 0.57

12. (a) 34.07   (b) $34\dfrac{7}{100}$

13. (a) $\angle b$ (b) $\angle d$

14. 0.0075

15. $7\dfrac{9}{10}$

16. $2\dfrac{5}{6}$

17. 10

18. $1\dfrac{2}{7}$

19. 9

20. 1.27

TEST 10 FORM A

1. $\dfrac{2}{7}$

2. 91

3. 0.376

4. 2

5. $\dfrac{11}{35}$

6. (a) $\dfrac{5}{8}$ (b) $\dfrac{3}{5}$

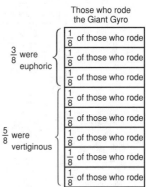

7. 22 cm

8. $6\dfrac{1}{4}$

9. 1.8

10. 52.23232

11. 6.8

12. $0.4\overline{7}$

13. 2

14. 3.86

15. 0.909

TEST ANSWERS

16. $8\frac{17}{20}$

17. $2\frac{1}{12}$

18. 72

19. $\frac{3}{8}$

20. 0.05

TEST 10 FORM B

1. $\frac{2}{5}$

2. 90

3. 0.385

4. 6

5. $\frac{1}{5}$

6. (a) $\frac{5}{9}$ (b) $\frac{4}{5}$

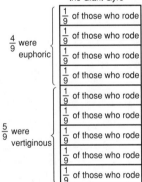

7. 18 cm

8. $6\frac{3}{4}$

9. 1.6

10. 15.5455

11. 6.6

12. $0.3\overline{7}$

13. 6

14. 2.86

15. 0.09

16. $9\frac{13}{20}$

17. $3\frac{5}{12}$

18. 81

19. $2\frac{2}{3}$

20. 0.1

TEST 11 FORM A

1. 1867

2. $2.25

3. $\frac{5}{12}$

4. $108

5. three and ninety-one hundredths

6. (a) $\frac{1}{8}$ (b) 9 buttons

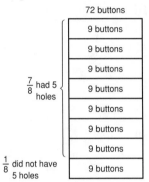

7. (a) 4 centimeters
   (b) $1\frac{5}{8}$ inches

8. $\frac{6}{25}$

9. $0.4\overline{36}$

10. $\frac{7}{8}$

11. 64 in.²

12. 24

13. 2.8

14. 3.64

15. 37

16. 2

17. $6\frac{13}{24}$

18. $1\frac{3}{7}$

19. 245

20. 1.255

TEST 11 FORM B

1. 1492

2. $2.55

3. $\frac{2}{5}$

4. $106

5. eighty-one hundredths

6. (a) $\frac{1}{6}$ (b) 12 buttons

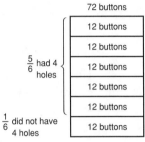

7. (a) 6 centimeters
   (b) $2\frac{3}{8}$ inches

8. $\frac{7}{25}$

9. $0.4\overline{45}$

10. $\frac{7}{9}$

11. 49 in.²

12. 33

13. 2.9

14. 3.58

15. 0

16. 2

17. $4\frac{1}{24}$

18. $2\frac{2}{5}$

19. 425

20. 12.6

TEST 12 FORM A

1. 347.3 miles

2. 48.823

3. 48

Math 87 by Hake & Saxon

4. (a) 2200 voters (b) $\dfrac{5}{4}$

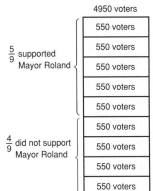

5. 70%

6. (a) $\dfrac{9}{50}$ (b) $1\dfrac{4}{5}$

7. (a) 375% (b) $33\dfrac{1}{3}\%$

8. 5 ft 10 in.

9. 30 yards

10. $66\dfrac{2}{7}$

11. 70 ft

12. 226 ft^2

13. 30

14. 1.74

15. $\dfrac{11}{12}$

16. 91

17. 3000

18. 135 miles

19. 5 yd 1 ft 1 in.

20. $1\dfrac{1}{12}$

TEST 12 FORM B

1. 338.4 miles

2. 54.833

3. 20

---

4. (a) 1860 voters (b) $\dfrac{5}{3}$

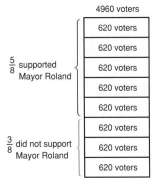

5. 30%

6. (a) $\dfrac{4}{25}$ (b) $1\dfrac{3}{5}$

7. (a) 275% (b) $66\dfrac{2}{3}\%$

8. 6 ft 3 in.

9. 90 feet

10. $51\dfrac{3}{7}$

11. 60 cm

12. 160 cm^2

13. $12\dfrac{1}{2}$

14. 0.48

15. $\dfrac{5}{6}$

16. 17

17. 500

18. 378 miles

19. 5 days 12 hr 3 min

20. $\dfrac{1}{2}$

TEST 13 FORM A

1. 45 skiffs

2. 128

3. $0.09

4. 1 inch

---

5. (a) 12 students (b) 30%

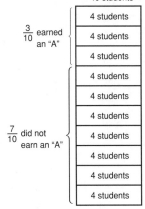

6. 4×10^{10}

7. 18,600,000

8. 80 cm

9. $4\dfrac{1}{10}$

10. 3 in.

11. 245 in.^{2}

12. 78 in.

13. 4.36

14. 36

15. 97

16. 9 yd 2 ft 2 in.

17. $8\dfrac{17}{24}$

18. $73\dfrac{1}{2}$

19. 0.001

20. 300

TEST 13 FORM B

1. 98 dinghies

2. 111

3. $0.05

4. 1 inch

5. (a) 16 students (b) 40%

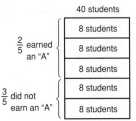

6. 1.4×10^{10}

7. 1,500,000
8. 60 cm
9. $3\frac{1}{2}$
10. 4 in.
11. 130 cm^2
12. 58 cm
13. 3.46
14. 2
15. 43
16. 4 yd 1 ft 5 in.
17. $8\frac{19}{24}$
18. 49
19. 0.01
20. 300

TEST 14 FORM A

1. $0.31
2. $1\frac{1}{3}$ cups
3. 53.4 seconds
4. 5 miles per hour
5. forty-nine million, six hundred eleven thousand
6. (a) 60%   (b) $\frac{2}{3}$

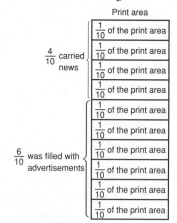

7. 2.05×10^{-3}
8. 0.0000562
9. 5280 ft
10. 4%
11. 64 cm
12. 180 cm^2

13. 6
14. 0.8
15. 109
16. 10,016
17. 2 yd 1 in.
18. $6\frac{11}{18}$
19. $12\frac{1}{2}$
20. 0.001075

TEST 14 FORM B

1. $0.32
2. $1\frac{1}{2}$ cups
3. 27.4 seconds
4. 7 miles per hour
5. nine million, four hundred fifty-one thousand
6. (a) 70%   (b) $\frac{3}{7}$

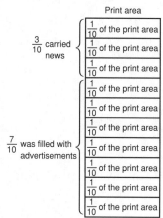

7. 4.05×10^{-3}
8. 0.0000625
9. 3960 ft
10. 5%
11. 50 in.
12. 140 in.^{2}
13. 15
14. 1.9
15. 29
16. 1003
17. 1 yd 1 ft 5 in.

18. $7\frac{5}{18}$
19. $2\frac{1}{4}$
20. 0.00055

TEST 15 FORM A

1. 11:05 a.m.
2. 60 miles per hour
3. 30 miles per gallon
4. 1690 fish
5. (a) 80%   (b) $\frac{1}{5}$

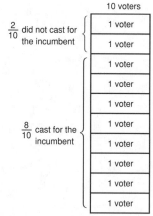

6. $3\frac{3}{5}$
7. 2×10^{-6}
8. 1,300,000
9. 324 in.
10.

```
        ┌──────────────→
        │
←───────┘
  ─┼──┼──┼──┼──┼──┼──┼──┼──┼─
  -4 -3 -2 -1  0  1 ②  3
```

11. (a) $\frac{3}{5}$ (b) 60%

    (c) $1\frac{1}{5}$ (d) 1.2
12. 10
13. 13 in.
14. 8 in.^{2}
15. 15
16. $\frac{5}{6}$
17. 5
18. 3 qt 14 oz

Math 87 by Hake & Saxon

19. $\frac{5}{6}$

20. 0.001

TEST 15 FORM B

1. 10:40 a.m.
2. 50 miles per hour
3. 25 miles per gallon
4. 450 reptiles
5. (a) 60%   (b) $\frac{2}{5}$

10 voters
| 1 voter |
$\frac{6}{10}$ cast for the incumbent
| 1 voter |
| 1 voter |
| 1 voter |
| 1 voter |
| 1 voter |
$\frac{4}{10}$ did not cast for the incumbent
| 1 voter |
| 1 voter |
| 1 voter |
| 1 voter |

6. $4\frac{4}{5}$
7. 3×10^{-6}
8. 150,000
9. 432 in.
10.

$-3\ -2\ -1\ \ 0\ \ 1\ \ 2\ \ ③\ \ 4$

11. (a) $\frac{4}{5}$ (b) 80%
    (c) $1\frac{2}{5}$ (d) 1.4
12. 16
13. 15 cm
14. 11 cm^2
15. 20
16. $\frac{7}{12}$
17. 15
18. 2 qt 1 pt 11 oz

19. $1\frac{2}{3}$

20. 1

TEST 16 FORM A

1. one hundred twenty-four ten-thousandths
2. $5.50
3. (a) $\frac{4}{7}$ (b) $\frac{3}{4}$
4. 3
5. 24
6. (a) 25%   (b) 177 stamps

236 stamps
gave $\frac{1}{4}$ to his sister
| 59 stamps |
had $\frac{3}{4}$ left
| 59 stamps |
| 59 stamps |
| 59 stamps |

7. 8×10^{-5}
8. 0.00024
9. =
10. 26
11. −7
12. (a) 0.125   (b) $12\frac{1}{2}$%
    (c) $\frac{3}{25}$ (d) 12%
13. 21 cm^2
14. $\frac{1}{2}$
15. 18
16. 0.05
17. 175
18. $5\frac{1}{12}$
19. 14
20. 0.06

TEST 16 FORM B

1. eleven thousandths
2. $6.50
3. (a) $\frac{2}{5}$ (b) $\frac{3}{2}$
4. 4
5. 51

6. (a) 20%   (b) 188 cards

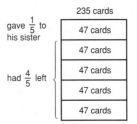

235 cards
gave $\frac{1}{5}$ to his sister
| 47 cards |
| 47 cards |
had $\frac{4}{5}$ left
| 47 cards |
| 47 cards |
| 47 cards |

7. 6×10^{-4}
8. 0.0075
9. >
10. 53
11. 4
12. (a) 0.375   (b) $37\frac{1}{2}$%
    (c) $\frac{3}{20}$ (d) 15%
13. 18 cm^2
14. $\frac{3}{5}$
15. 27
16. 1.5
17. 185
18. $4\frac{1}{2}$
19. $11\frac{5}{12}$
20. 0.012

TEST 17 FORM A

1. 6 minutes
2. 3
3. 588 students
4. 147 miles
5. (a) 300 pages   (b) $\frac{3}{5}$

480 pages
$\frac{3}{8}$ have been read
| 60 pages |
| 60 pages |
| 60 pages |
$\frac{5}{8}$ have not been read
| 60 pages |
| 60 pages |
| 60 pages |
| 60 pages |
| 60 pages |

6. (a) 31.4 cm   (b) 34π ft

7. 600 mm²

8. 750 mm²

9. 3.6×10^9

10. 400

11. 15

12. (a) $0.\overline{3}$ (b) $33\frac{1}{3}\%$

    (c) $\frac{8}{25}$ (d) 32%

13. −5

14. 20,000 pounds

15. 11

16. $1\frac{3}{8}$

17. 32

18. 295

19. 19

20. $1\frac{3}{22}$

Test 17 Form B

1. 5 minutes

2. 2

3. 338 students

4. 196 miles

5. (a) 135 pages (b) $\frac{5}{3}$

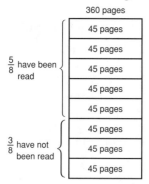

6. (a) 18.84 cm (b) 44 in.

7. 24 mm²

8. 30 mm²

9. 3.65×10^9

10. 300

11. 21

---

12. (a) $0.\overline{6}$ (b) $66\frac{2}{3}\%$

    (c) $\frac{9}{25}$ (d) 36%

13. −9

14. 32,000 pounds

15. 9

16. $1\frac{3}{8}$

17. 8

18. 493

19. 6

20. 3

Test 18 Form A

1. 24 kilometers per hour

2. 98 cats

3. a little too large, because $\pi > 3$

4. (a) $2.33 per pound
    (b) $23.30

5. 0.42

6. (a) 36 cookies (b) 40%

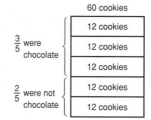

7. =

8. (a) 22π cm (b) 880 mm

9. (a) 1.1×10^{-6}
    (b) 1.1×10^8

10. 2.52

11. 210

12. $12\frac{1}{2}$

13. (a) $0.08\overline{3}$ (b) $8\frac{1}{3}\%$

    (c) $\frac{9}{50}$ (d) 0.18

14. −12

15. 8 kg

16. 0.1

17. 6.6

---

18. $6\frac{2}{5}$

19. 45.15

20. $\frac{4}{21}$

Test 18 Form B

1. 16 miles per hour

2. 45 cats

3. a little too large, because $\pi > 3$

4. (a) 41¢ per pound
    (b) $4.10

5. 0.76

6. (a) 24 cookies (b) 60%

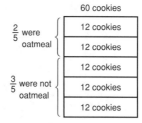

7. =

8. (a) 16π in. (b) 3.14 cm

9. (a) 1.2×10^{-5}
    (b) 1.2×10^7

10. 2.56

11. 180

12. 25

13. (a) $0.1\overline{6}$ (b) $16\frac{2}{3}\%$

    (c) $\frac{7}{50}$ (d) 0.14

14. −6

15. 9 kg

16. 0.04

17. 16.6

18. $5\frac{1}{2}$

19. 14.95

20. $\frac{2}{5}$

Test 19 Form A

1. 42 lifts

2. 4.8

3. 34 cm

4. 36 cm²

5. 14

6. 250 girls

7. 6400 milligrams

8. (a) 60 games
  (b) 40 games

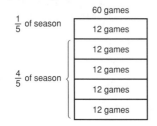

9. 90

10. 2010

11. (a) 18 (b) −54
  (c) 3 (d) −9

12. 125 cm³

13. (a) 132 m (b) 40π mm

14. (a) 0.2 (b) 20%
  (c) $\frac{9}{20}$ (d) 45%

15. 76

16. 12

17. 1.4

18. $\frac{\$15}{hr}$

19. −6

20. $\frac{9}{10}$

TEST 19 FORM B

1. 48 vows

2. 3.7

3. 26 cm

4. 21 cm²

5. 78

6. 200 girls

7. 4600 milligrams

8. (a) 48 games
  (b) 32 games

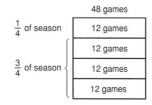

9. 96

10. 1200

11. (a) 24 (b) −18
  (c) 4 (d) −3

12. 27 cm³

13. (a) 62.8 cm (b) 30π in.

14. (a) 0.60 (b) 60%
  (c) $\frac{7}{20}$ (d) 35%

15. 51

16. 16

17. 2.4

18. $\frac{\$12.50}{hr}$

19. −5

20. $1\frac{1}{8}$

TEST 20 FORM A

1. $\frac{\$3.80}{hr}$

2. 6

3. >

4. 15 articles of clothing

5. 960 customers

6. 47 m

7. 7 pints

8. [number line from −6 to 1, open circle at −5]

9. 56 inches

10. (a) −80 (b) 60
  (c) −300 (d) 960

11. (a) $0.8\overline{3}$ (b) $83\frac{1}{3}\%$
  (c) $\frac{3}{5}$ (d) 60%

12. 1350

13. 14

14. $\frac{4}{75}$

15. 36 m²

16. 80

17. 1.58

18. 5

19. $3\frac{1}{3}$

20. 51

TEST 20 FORM B

1. $\frac{\$3.87}{hr}$

2. 12

3. =

4. 10 articles of clothing

5. 720 customers

6. 44 m

7. 5 pints

8. [number line from −6 to 1, filled dot at −5]

9. 64 inches

10. (a) −60 (b) 70
  (c) −450 (d) 720

11. (a) $0.\overline{1}$ (b) $11\frac{1}{9}\%$
  (c) $\frac{4}{5}$ (d) 80%

12. 1080

13. 21

14. $\frac{1}{15}$

15. 22 m²

16. 75

17. 2.57

18. 1

19. $\frac{3}{10}$

20. −2

TEST 21 FORM A

1. 6 games

2. (a) 77 (b) 75
  (c) 60, 70, and 80 (d) 40

3. 99 dandelions

4. 470 milliliters

5.

6. 24 miles

7. 180 children

8. (a) $50,000   (b) 10%

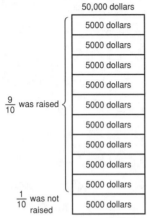

9. insufficient information

10. 24 in.³

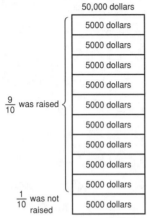

11. 113.04 in.²

12. (a) 0.075   (b) $7\frac{1}{2}$%

(c) $\frac{1}{30}$ (d) $0.0\overline{3}$

13. parallelogram; 49 cm

14. 140 cm²

15. 3.25×10^{15}

16. 11

17. $\frac{34}{45}$

18. 12

19. $\frac{3}{20}$

20. −8

TEST 21 FORM B

1. 15 grams

2. (a) 67   (b) 65
(c) 50, 60, and 70
(d) 40

3. 81 dandelions

---

4. 840 milliliters

5.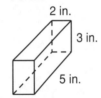

6. 25 seconds

7. 200 children

8. (a) $60,000   (b) 30%

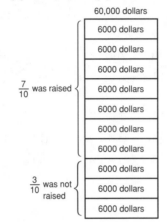

9. <

10. 30 in.³

11. 154 in.²

12. (a) 0.15   (b) 15%

(c) $\frac{1}{60}$ (d) $0.01\overline{6}$

13. parallelogram; 98 mm

14. 560 mm²

15. 3.6×10^{13}

16. 12

17. $1\frac{11}{45}$

18. 0

19. $\frac{3}{10}$

20. −8

TEST 22 FORM A

1. 8 bears

2. 3000 cm³

3. 0.421

4. 9 yd²

5.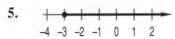

6. (a) $48.00   (b) 75%

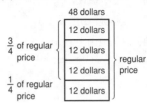

7. 55°

8. 55°

9. 88 in.

10. 400 mm²

11. <

12. (a) $\frac{3}{50}$ (b) 6%

13. 2750 customers

14. 20%

15. 60°

16. 1×10^{-7}

17. 252

18. 6.57

19. 21

20. −5

TEST 22 FORM B

1. 18 bears

2. 4500 cm³

3. 0.412

4. 6 yd²

5.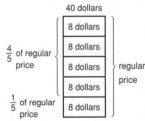

6. (a) $40   (b) 80%

7. 55°

8. 55°

9. 94.2 in.

10. 500 mm²

11. <

12. (a) $\frac{2}{25}$ (b) 8%

13. 1650 customers

14. 40%

15. 45°

16. 1×10^{-8}

17. 324

18. 11.25

19. 420

20. −7

Test 23 Form A

1. 96

2. $\frac{7}{9}$

3. $8

4. 300,000

5. 40¢ per pound

6. 75%

7. 100,000 mm²

8. −13

9. 150 mm²

10. (a) $5.76   (b) $101.76

11. 2.8×10^5

12. (a) $3.\overline{3}$ (b) $333\frac{1}{3}\%$

     (c) $\frac{1}{50}$ (d) 0.02

13.
```
 ──┼──┼──●──●──●──┼──┼──►
  -2  -1  0  1  2  3  4
```

14. 36

15. 5.85

16. 50

17. 800 milliliters

18. $2\frac{5}{6}$

19. 8

20. −26

Test 23 Form B

1. 98

2. $\frac{3}{5}$

3. $12

4. 360,000

5. 60¢ per pound

6. 80%

7. 1000 mm²

8. −9

9. 210 cm²

10. (a) $7.44   (b) $131.44

11. 1.6×10^8

12. (a) $1.\overline{3}$ (b) $133\frac{1}{3}\%$

     (c) $\frac{1}{25}$ (d) 0.04

13.
```
 ──┼──┼──●──●──●──●──►
  -2  -1  0  1  2  3  4
```

14. 18

15. 4.55

16. 96

17. 900 milligrams

18. $5\frac{1}{6}$

19. −8

20. −21

Test 24 Form A

1. 85.5

2. $\frac{\$9}{\text{hr}}$

3. 140%

4. 16,000 cm²

5. (a) 30 eggs   (b) $83\frac{1}{3}\%$

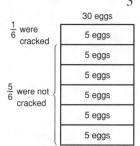

6. 5

7. 9 in.²

8. (a) $\frac{1}{3}$ (b) $\frac{2}{3}$

9. 72 cm³

10. 314 cm²

11. $381.60

12. $14.00

13. 60°

14. 3.2×10^{-4}

15. 5.5

16. 36

17. 100

18. 4 yd 5 in.

19. $1\frac{1}{2}$

20. −7

Test 24 Form B

1. 86.5

2. $\frac{\$8}{\text{hr}}$

3. 130%

4. 24,000 cm²

5. (a) 18   (b) $83\frac{1}{3}\%$

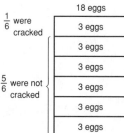

6. 7

7. 36 in.²

8. (a) $\frac{2}{3}$ (b) $\frac{1}{3}$

9. 96 cm³

10. 616 in.²

11. $342.40

12. $16.00

13. 120°

14. 2.1×10^{-4}

15. 10.5

16. 18

17. 83

18. 3 yd 3 in.

19. $8\frac{1}{10}$

20. −13

TEST 25 FORM A

1. $3.60
2. 80 kilometers per hour
3. 576 inches = 48 feet
4. $175.00
5. $45.00
6. $3.12
7. (a) (4, –1)   (b) 24 units^2
8. 10 inches
9. 12 cm^3
10. 282.6 cm^3
11. 9
12. 41°
13. –3, $\sqrt{3}$, 3, 3^2
14. 113.04 in.^{2}
15. B
16. 3
17. 1.6
18. 15
19. 6
20. 24

TEST 25 FORM B

1. $2.70
2. 600 miles per hour
3. 450 inches = $37\frac{1}{2}$ feet
4. $75.00
5. $65.00
6. $5.46
7. (a) (3, 2)   (b) 16 units^2
8. 8 in.
9. 96 cm^3
10. 251.2 cm^3
11. 9
12. 52°
13. –5, $\sqrt{5}$, 5, 5^2
14. 154 in.^{2}
15. C
16. 6
17. 2.4
18. 6

19. 8
20. 2

TEST 26 FORM A

1. (a) 89   (b) 88.5
   (c) 88   (d) 11
2. $\dfrac{1}{26}$
3. $140.00
4. 75 marbles
5. $78 per day
6. $6.00
7. 3500
8. 6 units^2
9. 9.01
10. $y = 2x - 1$

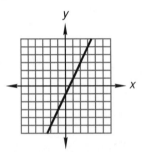

11. 21.42 cm
12. 15,700 cm^3
13. 54 in.^{2}
14. 20°
15. 12
16. 36
17. 4
18. 80
19. $13\frac{3}{4}$
20. –7

TEST 26 FORM B

1. (a) 94   (b) 93
   (c) 93   (d) 10
2. $\dfrac{2}{13}$
3. $640.00
4. 462 peanuts
5. $91 per day
6. $3.40

7. 1750
8. 16 units^2
9. 10.16
10. $y = 2x + 1$

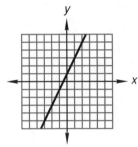

11. 33.7 cm
12. 18.84 cm^3
13. 24 in.^{2}
14. 40°
15. 4
16. 18
17. 2.5
18. 94
19. $21\frac{2}{3}$
20. –35

TEST 27 FORM A

1. $14.70
2. $64.75
3. $30.00
4. 9.1 × 10^9
5. 0.94
6. $\dfrac{1}{8}$
7. 15%
8. $480.00
9. 6 units^2
10. 576 in.^{2}
11. 40 yards
12. 6000 m^3

Math 87 by Hake & Saxon

13. $y = -x + 2$

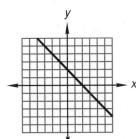

14. 4

15. 60°

16. 25

17. 6

18. 640

19. $3\frac{1}{12}$

20. 2

18. 780

19. $5\frac{1}{15}$

20. 4

TEST 27 FORM B

1. $15.75

2. $71.75

3. $28.00

4. 9.2×10^9

5. 1.04

6. $\frac{1}{16}$

7. 25%

8. $560.00

9. 6 units²

10. 54 ft²

11. 10 yd

12. 1570 in.³

13. $y = -x - 1$

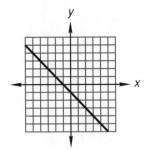

14. 8

15. 20°

16. 9

17. 3.5

QUIZ 1

1. 11
2. $14.97
3. $3.50
4. 54
5. 279

QUIZ 2

1. 4
2. $40.55
3. 31
4. 61
5. 14

QUIZ 3

1. −3, −1, 0, 2
2. >
3. 68
4. 45
5. 11

QUIZ 4

1.
2. (a) > (b) =
3. 297
4. 185
5. 20

QUIZ 5

1. thirty-seven million, five hundred twenty-eight thousand, four hundred
2. $4.31
3. 254
4. 610
5. 18

QUIZ 6

1. 350,035,009
2. 1, 3, 7, 21
3. 1, 2, 3, 5, 6, 10
4. 288
5. 24

QUIZ 7

1. five billion, three hundred twenty million, one hundred five thousand, sixty
2. 1, 2, 3, 4, 5, 6, 8, 9, 10
3. $\overline{QR}, \overline{RS}, \overline{QS}$
4. 405
5. 776

QUIZ 8

1. 10,600,053,000
2. 1, 2, 3, 4, 5, 6, 7, 9, 10
3.
4. numerator
5. $1\frac{3}{4} < 2\frac{1}{3}$

QUIZ 9

1. thirty billion, one hundred two million, fifty thousand, seven hundred six
2. (a) 1, 2, 4, 8, 16
   (b) 1, 2, 3, 4, 6, 8, 12, 24
   (c) 1, 2, 4, 8
3. $4\frac{1}{3}$
4. $\frac{5}{7}$
5. $\frac{9}{20}$

QUIZ 10

1. 10,100,001,110
2. >
3. 1, 2, 3, 5, 6, 9
4. 0
5. $\frac{1}{8}$

QUIZ 11

1. 658 runners
2. $-3, 0, \frac{1}{3}, 1$
3. one billion, thirty million, forty thousand, five
4. $\frac{7}{8}$
5. $\frac{18}{35}$

QUIZ 12

1. 109 years
2. $35.40
3. 64,000
4. 0
5. $\frac{9}{100}$

QUIZ 13

1. 155 tickets
2. 110,000,200,000
3. $5\frac{5}{9}$
4. $\frac{3}{8}$
5. 2

QUIZ 14

1. $\frac{3}{4}$
2. 66,000
3.
4. 1, 2, 4, 5, 10, 20, 25, 50, 100
5. 100

QUIZ 15

1. $\frac{8}{8}$
2. (a) $1\frac{3}{5}$ (b) 2

3. 250 boxes

4.

5. 1

QUIZ 16

1. $\dfrac{5}{10}$

2. 2,770,000

3. $-1, 0, \dfrac{2}{3}, 1, \dfrac{3}{2}$

4. (a) 8   (b) 9

5. $1\dfrac{1}{9}$

QUIZ 17

1. $\dfrac{3}{5}$

2. (a) $\dfrac{1}{3}$ (b) $4\dfrac{2}{3}$

3. (a) $\dfrac{10}{12}$ (b) $\dfrac{9}{12}$

4. $1\dfrac{3}{5}$

5. $\dfrac{2}{5}$

QUIZ 18

1. $3\dfrac{2}{3}$

2. (a) $\dfrac{15}{18}$ (b) $\dfrac{10}{18}$

3. 1, 2, 4, 5, 8

4. $\dfrac{1}{3}$

5. $\dfrac{2}{5}$

QUIZ 19

1. ; right angles

2. $\dfrac{5}{8}$

3. (a) 6   (b) 5

4. $2\dfrac{2}{5}$

5. $\dfrac{1}{4}$

QUIZ 20

1. 999,000,000

2. ; triangle

3. (a) $\dfrac{8}{20}$ (b) $\dfrac{15}{20}$

4. 3

5. $2\dfrac{1}{4}$

QUIZ 21

1. 24 inches

2. (a) 25   (b) 9

3. octagon

4. $\dfrac{1}{2}$

5. $\dfrac{3}{8}$

QUIZ 22

1. 1000 feet

2. $-2, 0, \dfrac{1}{4}, \dfrac{1}{2}, 1$

3. 14

4. 16

5. 56

QUIZ 23

1. $2 \cdot 2 \cdot 2 \cdot 3 \cdot 3$

2. 4 cm

3. (a) 20   (b) 21

4. 16

5. 17

QUIZ 24

1. $2 \cdot 2 \cdot 3 \cdot 3 \cdot 5 \cdot 5$

2. 6 cm

3. $1\dfrac{3}{4}$

4. 90

5. 12

QUIZ 25

1. $2 \cdot 3 \cdot 3 \cdot 3 \cdot 5$

2. 36 inches

3. (a) $\dfrac{7}{2}$ (b) $\dfrac{3}{1}$

4. (a) 15   (b) 10

5. $\dfrac{2}{3}$

QUIZ 26

1. (a) 12   (b) 16

2. 9 inches

3. (a) $\dfrac{21}{4}$ (b) $\dfrac{5}{1}$

4. 1

5. 25

QUIZ 27

1. (a) 20   (b) 16

2. 6 cm

3. $4\dfrac{1}{3}$

4. $2\dfrac{3}{5}$

5. (a) 15   (b) 14

QUIZ 28

1. $2 \cdot 2 \cdot 3 \cdot 3 \cdot 7$

2. $\dfrac{2}{5}$

3. 6 inches

4. $7\dfrac{1}{4}$

5. $3\dfrac{1}{3}$

QUIZ 29

1. $\dfrac{14}{25}$

2. (a) $\dfrac{1}{4}$ (b) $\dfrac{5}{13}$

3. $\dfrac{1}{3}$

4. $10\dfrac{1}{2}$

5. $1\dfrac{3}{4}$

QUIZ 30

1. $\dfrac{3}{5}$

2. $\dfrac{1}{12}$

3. $5\dfrac{1}{2}$

4. $5\dfrac{5}{8}$

5. $\dfrac{9}{20}$

QUIZ 31

1. $\dfrac{3}{20}$

2. $8\dfrac{1}{3}$

3. $1\dfrac{1}{3}$

4. $6\dfrac{1}{3}$

5. $4\dfrac{1}{3}$

QUIZ 32

1. 24

2. $3\dfrac{8}{9}$

3. $\dfrac{7}{20}$

4. $3\dfrac{1}{4}$

5. $\dfrac{1}{2}$

QUIZ 33

1. $3.75

2. 36

3. $10\dfrac{1}{8}$

4. $1\dfrac{1}{8}$

5. $10\dfrac{1}{8}$

QUIZ 34

1. 44

2. 8

3. 6

4. $1\dfrac{1}{24}$

5. $1\dfrac{2}{3}$

QUIZ 35

1. (a) 2000   (b) 1800

2. 461

3. 27

4. $1\dfrac{1}{3}$

5. $1\dfrac{1}{2}$

QUIZ 36

1. (a) 4000   (b) 3800

2. $\dfrac{7}{8}$

3. $\dfrac{7}{12}$

4. $4\dfrac{5}{6}$

5. $3\dfrac{1}{3}$

QUIZ 37

1. (a) 500   (b) 530

2. $4\dfrac{1}{2}$

3. $2\dfrac{1}{12}$

4. 2

5. 3

QUIZ 38

1. 20.05

2. $5\dfrac{1}{2}$

3. $2\dfrac{1}{2}$

4. 32

5. $\dfrac{8}{9}$

QUIZ 39

1. (a) 14.29   (b) 14

2. 91

3. $2\dfrac{1}{8}$

4. $3\dfrac{2}{3}$

5. $\dfrac{2}{5}$

QUIZ 40

1. (a) 16.7   (b) 17

2. 1.25

3. 10

4. 12

5. $3\dfrac{5}{8}$

QUIZ 41

1. 0.13

2. 12.55

3. 11.25

4. $2\frac{1}{2}$

5. $3\frac{1}{9}$

QUIZ 42

1. (a) $\frac{2}{3}$ (b) $\frac{3}{2}$

2. 18.18

3. 2.137

4. $6\frac{3}{10}$

5. 6

QUIZ 43

1. $\frac{3}{2}$

2. 40 cm

3. 6.54

4. $6\frac{5}{6}$

5. $1\frac{1}{11}$

QUIZ 44

1. $\frac{3}{8}$

2. (a) 4   (b) 21

3. 27.88

4. $10\frac{4}{15}$

5. $1\frac{1}{3}$

QUIZ 45

1. 3

2. 16

3. 9.972

4. $2\frac{9}{10}$

5. 5

QUIZ 46

1. 9

2. 0.0075

3. 0.82

4. $2\frac{1}{4}$

5. $2\frac{1}{8}$

QUIZ 47

1. 18

2. 0.3

3. 0.018

4. 16

5. $3\frac{5}{6}$

QUIZ 48

1. (a) $0.1\overline{5}$ (b) 0.16

2. $\frac{5}{7}$

3. 2

4. 0.006

5. $10\frac{7}{8}$

QUIZ 49

1. (a) $\frac{1}{8}$ (b) $25\frac{1}{25}$

2. (a) 3.3   (b) 5.2

3. 0.778

4. $5\frac{1}{4}$

5. 0.017

QUIZ 50

1. (a) 1 r 8   (b) $1.\overline{8}$

2. $\frac{2}{7}$

3. $2.\overline{6}$

4. $46\frac{14}{15}$

5. 4.585

QUIZ 51

1. 23.8

2. 206.5

3. 9

4. 44 feet per second

5. $1\frac{9}{16}$

QUIZ 52

1. 12¢ per ounce

2. $\frac{3}{2}$

3. 152.8

4. $5\frac{1}{20}$

5. 1.62

QUIZ 53

1. (a) "two cubed" or "two to the third power"
(b) "five to the fifth power"

2. (a) 32   (b) 7

3. 24-ounce bottle is a better buy

4. $2.\overline{7}$

5. 1.262

QUIZ 54

1. $(6 \times 10^2) + (4 \times 10^1) + (9 \times 10^0)$

2. 185,700

3. (a) 72,113.273   (b) 72,000

4. 5.875

5. 0.00056

QUIZ 55

1. 25 m^2

2. 21 cm^2

3. $(3 \times 10^3) + (1 \times 10^2) + (4 \times 10^1)$

4. $0.95 per pound

5. 142

Quiz 56

1. (a) 12   (b) 9
2. 64 cm²
3. 37
4. 8.33
5. $10\frac{1}{6}$

Quiz 57

1. (a) $62\frac{\text{miles}}{\text{hour}}$; $\frac{1\text{ hour}}{62\text{ miles}}$

   (b) $62\frac{\text{miles}}{\text{hour}}$
2. 18¢ per ounce
3. 36 in.²
4. 3
5. 736

Quiz 58

1. (a) $\frac{3}{20}$ (b) $1\frac{3}{4}$
2. (a) 5%   (b) 300%
3. $27\frac{\text{francs}}{\text{dollar}}$
4. 25
5. 20

Quiz 59

1. 6 ft 1 in.
2. 6 yd
3. $3\frac{1}{5}$
4. 93
5. 5280

Quiz 60

1. (a) $300\frac{\text{miles}}{\text{hour}}$; $\frac{1\text{ hour}}{300\text{ miles}}$

   (b) 5 hours
2. 30 cm²
3. 8 hr 59 sec
4. 130
5. 15%

Quiz 61

1. 350 cm²
2. (a) $60\frac{\text{words}}{\text{minute}}$; $\frac{1\text{ minute}}{60\text{ words}}$

   (b) 1800 words
3. 8 hr 46 min 10 sec
4. 6 yd 2 ft 5 in.
5. 95

Quiz 62

1. (a) 2×10^{4}
   (b) 4.5×10^{9}
2. (a) 180,000,000
   (b) 2,400,000
3. 135 m²
4. 10 days 3 hr 45 min
5. 26

Quiz 63

1. 11
2. 2
3. 1×10^{9}
4. (a) $5\frac{\text{meters}}{\text{second}}$; $\frac{1\text{ second}}{5\text{ meters}}$

   (b) 125 meters
5. 75

Quiz 64

1. 45 feet
2. 2500 centimeters
3. 5 feet
4. 18
5. 4

Quiz 65

1. 50 chipmunks
2. 14 sloops
3. 15
4. 8 yards
5. 17.13

Quiz 66

1. 13
2. 91

3. 45 carnivores
4. 12 feet
5. 28

Quiz 67

1. 1 ft 11 in.
2. 1 day 22 hr 5 min
3. 12 ranchers
4. 101
5. 65

Quiz 68

1. 1300 mL
2. 5 gallons
3. $1.20
4. 1 qt 1 pt 13 oz
5. 16 photographs

Quiz 69

1. (a) 2×10^{-7}
   (b) 5×10^{-3}
2. (a) 0.0000073
   (b) 0.0004
3. 4 quarts
4. 16.927
5. 37

Quiz 70

1. True
2. False
3. 3.14×10^{-5}
4. $\frac{1}{8}$
5. 2 weeks 2 days 11 hr

Quiz 71

1. perimeter = 80 cm
   area = 336 cm²
2. (a) rectangle
   (b) trapezoid
3. 1760 yards
4. 6 gallons
5. 3.06

QUIZ 72

1. (a) $\frac{3}{20}$ (b) 15%
2. perimeter = 160 cm
   area = 1250 cm²
3. 600 angiosperms
4. liter
5. 1 hr 40 min 18 sec

QUIZ 73

1. $\frac{1}{2}, \frac{1}{4}, \frac{1}{8}$
2. 25
3. (a) $\frac{5}{6}$ (b) 45%
4. 0.000024
5. 329.7

QUIZ 74

1.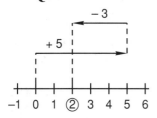
2. 12, 16, 20
3. (a) $\frac{7}{20}$ (b) 0.35
4. 300,000,000
5. 7.5

QUIZ 75

1. 24
2. 28
3.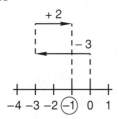
4. (a) 0.375 (b) $37\frac{1}{2}$%
5. 25, 36, 49

QUIZ 76

1. 4
2. $\frac{1}{6}$
3. 58
4. 3 gal 1 qt 1 pt 4 oz
5. 75 centimeters

QUIZ 77

1. (a) right (b) acute
2. (a) isosceles (b) scalene
3. 45
4. 901 mL
5. $5280\frac{\text{ft}}{\text{min}}$

QUIZ 78

1. 75
2. 5
3. 72
4. $\frac{1}{6}$
5. $0.4\overline{45}$

QUIZ 79

1. −100
2. 25
3. 48
4. 16 cm
5. 124

QUIZ 80

1. 24 cm²
2. 15 cm²
3. 25
4. $7\frac{1}{2}$
5. 3240 mL

QUIZ 81

1. 36
2. 1
3. 8 pounds

4. 4
5. 75 cm

QUIZ 82

1. 80 lily pads
2. 50 girls
3. 9
4. 4.25
5. 3

QUIZ 83

1. (a) cube (b) pyramid
2. (a) 5 (b) 8
3. 45 red apples
4. 6
5. 2

QUIZ 84

1. 48 ounces
2. 50,000 milligrams
3. (a) 9 (b) 6
4. 133
5. 12

QUIZ 85

1. 800 centimeters
2. 24 inches
3. 9 pounds
4. 9 lb 13 oz
5. 5 gal 1 pt 14 oz

QUIZ 86

1. (a) 31.4 cm (b) 16π m
2. 80 ounces
3. 51
4. 1550 grams
5. 3

QUIZ 87

1. −10
2. 4
3. 43.96 cm
4. 65 rings
5. 1 lb 5 oz

Quiz Answers

Quiz 88

1. $2\frac{1}{8}$
2. 6.325
3. 0
4. 16 feet
5. 21

Quiz 89

1. 519
2. 54
3. $6\frac{5}{8}$
4. 52 dancers
5. 1884 meters

Quiz 90

1. (a) 3.4×10^7
   (b) 2.7×10^{-5}
2. 73
3. 2 yards
4. $3\frac{11}{20}$
5. 8 yd 1 ft 9 in.

Quiz 91

1. 24
2. $\frac{3}{5}$
3. 4.3×10^7
4. 44
5. $60\frac{mi}{hr}$

Quiz 92

1. 180 cm³
2. 19
3. (a) 5×10^{-6}
   (b) 1.8×10^{-13}
4. 3500 milliliters
5. 12

Quiz 93

1. 3584 stars
2. 45 1-cm cubes
3. 5.7×10^{-6}
4. 62.8 inches
5. 13

Quiz 94

1. 20 minutes
2. 112 bales
3. 112 ounces
4. 1 gal 3 qt 1 pt
5. 1

Quiz 95

1. 184
2. 0.15
3. 15 hours
4. 1.8×10^{-5}
5. 2

Quiz 96

1. -30
2. 4
3. 108
4. 12 shrubs
5. 5×10^{-3}

Quiz 97

1. 76 cm²
2. $\frac{1}{3}$
3. 7 hr 12 min 59 sec
4. 132
5. -15

Quiz 98

1. (a) 32 (b) $\frac{1}{8}$
2. (a) $\frac{1}{36}$ (b) $\frac{5}{6}$
3. 45 cm²
4. -91
5. 1

Quiz 99

1. 25%
2. $16\frac{2}{3}\%$
3. $\frac{1}{18}$
4. 25
5. 455 doctors

Quiz 100

1.
2.
3. $70\frac{5}{6}\%$
4. $\frac{5}{12}$
5. 18 holes

Quiz 101

1. insufficient information
2. $>$
3.
4. $22\frac{2}{9}\%$
5. 3

Quiz 102

1. (a) 135° (b) 150°
   (c) 30°
2. $<$
3.
4. 25
5. 1.82

Quiz 103

1. $120,000
2. 70%
3.

34 *Math 87* by Hake and Saxon

4. 6.5×10^4

5. (a) 16   (b) -4

QUIZ 104

1. 200.96 cm²

2. 43 students

3.
$$-5 \; -4 \; -3 \; -2 \; -1$$

4. insufficient information

5. -15

QUIZ 105

1. (a) 4.452×10^7
   (b) 7.2×10^{-11}

2. 254.34 cm²

3. 70%

4.
$$-3 \; -2 \; -1 \; 0 \; 1$$

5. -7

QUIZ 106

1. (a) 92   (b) 91
   (c) 88   (d) 15

2. 3.5×10^4

3. 314 in.²

4. -2

5. 60

QUIZ 107

1. 7

2.
x	y
3	3
8	13
0	-3

3. 8 feet

4. 6 miles

5. 2.58×10^3

QUIZ 108

1. False

2. True

3.
$$-1 \; 0 \; 1 \; 2 \; 3 \; 4 \; 5 \; 6$$

---

4. 56

5. -6

QUIZ 109

1. (a) $33\frac{1}{3}\%$ (b) $87\frac{1}{2}\%$

2. (a) $\frac{4}{5}$ (b) $\frac{5}{6}$

3.
$$-3 \; -2 \; -1 \; 0 \; 1$$

4. $24

5. -2

QUIZ 110

1. (a) 2880 in.²
   (b) 8100 seconds

2. 40 trumpets

3. (a) -116 (b) 2 yd 7 in.

4. (a) -1 (b) 0.00052

5. 2450

QUIZ 111

1. $A = 45°$; $B = 45°$;
   $M = 135°$; $R = 135°$

2. 12 pigs

3. (a) $30   (b) 80%

4.
$$-4 \; -3 \; -2 \; -1 \; 0$$

5. (a) $0.58\overline{3}$ (b) $58\frac{1}{3}\%$

QUIZ 112

1. (a) $\frac{25}{32}$ (b) 80

2. 92%

3. (a) $6\frac{7}{12}$ (b) 6.5
   (c) 5   (d) 7

4. two hundred twenty-five
   thousandths

5. 60 in.³

QUIZ 113

1. (a) -3 (b) -5

2. (a) -9 (b) -2

3. 110 people

4. (a) trapezoid   (b) 66 cm
   (c) 252 cm²

5. 2.88×10^{-9}

QUIZ 114

1. (a) $3.33   (b) $50.83

2. $12.81

3. insufficient information

4. $36.75

5. (a) 130°   (b) 20°
   (c) 125°   (d) 55°

QUIZ 115

1. (a) 104   (b) 25

2. 30 yd²

3. (a) $\frac{3}{8}$ (b) 0.375

4.
x	y
3	11
-2	-9
5	19

5. 88 m

QUIZ 116

1. $28.50

2. 517,500

3. 95

4. =

5. (a) 64   (b) 675 mL

QUIZ 117

1. (a) 3   (b) 5

2. (a) 9   (b) 2

3. (a) 25   (b) $58\frac{1}{3}\%$

4. $12.84

5. $166\frac{3}{8}$ in.³

QUIZ 118

1. $\frac{1}{2}$

2. $\frac{1}{4}$

3. (a) 840 hr   (b) 36 ft²

4. 378 cm²

5. (a) 3   (b) 6.5

QUIZ 119

1. 12 cm³

2. 3300 cm³

3. 20 kilometers per hour

4. $4

5.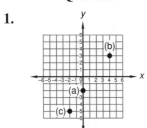

QUIZ 120

1.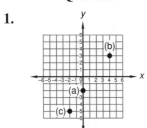

2. 3.822×10^{-1}

3. (a) $\frac{1}{4}$ (b) $\frac{1}{26}$

4. (a) $6.24   (b) $84.24

5. 4872 yd³

QUIZ 121

1. (a) 168°   (b) 90°
   (c) 78°

2. insufficient information

3. 275

4. (a) $\frac{5}{60}$ (b) $0.08\overline{3}$

5. 324 in.²

QUIZ 122

1. $x = 3$; $y = 28$

2. $87\frac{1}{2}\%$

3. (a) 94.2 cm
   (b) 706.5 cm²

4. 6.58×10^{12}

5. $x = 47°$; $y = 98°$;
   $z = 57°$

QUIZ 123

1. $5\frac{1}{4}$ inches

2. (a) 81   (b) 3

3. (a) 150%   (b) $14.70

4.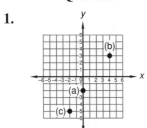
   -6 -5 -4 -3 -2 -1 0

5. −3

QUIZ 124

1. 12

2. 20

3. 12 feet

4. 27

5. 2

QUIZ 125

1. (a) 7 and 8   (b) 8 and 9

2. (a) complementary
   (b) supplementary

3. 8

4. 40

5. 189 ft²

QUIZ 126

1. 240

2. −243

3. (a) 11 and 12
   (b) 9 and 10

4. 120°

5. 392.5 cm³

QUIZ 127

1. 85.7 in.

2. 239.25 in.²

3. 35°

4. −23

5. 300

QUIZ 128

1. 312 cm²

2. 260.48 in.²

3. 1 yd²

4. −20

5. 1320 yd

QUIZ 129

1. $w = x + y$

2. $b = \frac{2A}{h}$

3. 336 cm²

4. 1.53×10^{-3}

5. −30

QUIZ 130

1.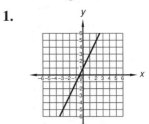

2.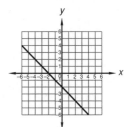

3. $x = 2b - w$

4. $a = \frac{2d}{t^2}$

5. 5

QUIZ 131

1. 6

2. 20

3.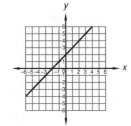

4. $y = mx + b$

5. 40

QUIZ 132

1. $450

2. $2320

3. 9

4. 150°

5. −16

QUIZ 133

1. $\dfrac{1}{8}$

2. $\dfrac{1}{12}$

3. $6050

4. $\dfrac{1}{12}$

5. 10.5

QUIZ 134

1. 251.2 cm^3

2. 297 cm^3

3. $\dfrac{1}{104}$

4. −6

5. 50

QUIZ 135

1. (a) $\dfrac{3}{8}$ (b) 19 to 5

2. 2 to 3

3. 84.78 m^3

4. $x = \dfrac{y - b}{m}$

5. 15

Math 87
Test Masters

Speed Test Forms

Instructions

Begin the class with a speed test and limit the test to five minutes or less. The rule of thumb for timing speed tests is one minute for every 20 questions. For example, five minutes for a 100-question speed drill is a good beginning. Mental processes become fully automated after breaking this five-minute barrier. Students' performance on the tests also becomes markedly better after breaking this barrier. Two to three days after the students break the five-minute mark, their speed is often down to four minutes. The time element is very important.

Copy the speed test for each student. Begin by saying, "Ready, set, go," and time the students carefully. At the beginning of the year, quickly go over the answers. There is no need to re-read every question; just read the answers rapidly. Later, it is not necessary to go over the questions daily. Initially, the challenge is to generate the proper response to the question. With practice, the challenge is no longer to get the right answer but rather to complete the task as quickly as possible. The students are racing to beat their previous records. Students should be asked to record their times at the top of the page.

Test A—100 Addition Facts   Name _____   Time _____

3 + 2	8 + 3	2 + 1	5 + 6	2 + 9	4 + 8	8 + 0	3 + 9	1 + 0	6 + 3
7 + 3	1 + 6	4 + 7	0 + 3	6 + 4	5 + 5	3 + 1	7 + 2	8 + 5	2 + 5
4 + 0	5 + 7	1 + 1	5 + 4	2 + 8	7 + 1	4 + 6	0 + 2	6 + 5	4 + 9
8 + 6	0 + 4	5 + 8	7 + 4	1 + 7	6 + 6	4 + 1	8 + 2	2 + 4	6 + 0
9 + 1	8 + 8	2 + 2	4 + 5	6 + 2	0 + 0	5 + 9	3 + 3	8 + 1	2 + 7
4 + 4	7 + 5	0 + 1	8 + 7	3 + 4	7 + 9	1 + 2	6 + 7	0 + 8	9 + 2
0 + 9	8 + 9	7 + 6	1 + 3	6 + 8	2 + 0	8 + 4	3 + 5	9 + 8	5 + 0
9 + 3	2 + 6	3 + 0	6 + 1	3 + 6	5 + 2	0 + 5	6 + 9	1 + 8	9 + 6
4 + 3	9 + 9	0 + 7	9 + 4	7 + 7	1 + 4	3 + 7	7 + 0	2 + 3	5 + 1
9 + 5	1 + 5	9 + 0	3 + 8	1 + 9	5 + 3	4 + 2	9 + 7	0 + 6	7 + 8

MATH 87   by Hake and Saxon

16 − 9	7 − 1	18 − 9	11 − 3	13 − 7	8 − 2	11 − 5	5 − 0	17 − 9	6 − 1
10 − 9	6 − 2	13 − 4	4 − 0	10 − 5	5 − 1	10 − 3	12 − 6	10 − 1	6 − 4
7 − 2	14 − 7	8 − 1	11 − 6	3 − 3	16 − 7	5 − 2	12 − 4	3 − 0	11 − 7
17 − 8	6 − 0	10 − 6	4 − 1	9 − 5	9 − 0	5 − 4	12 − 5	4 − 2	9 − 3
12 − 3	16 − 8	9 − 1	15 − 6	11 − 4	13 − 5	1 − 0	8 − 5	9 − 6	11 − 2
7 − 0	10 − 8	6 − 3	14 − 5	3 − 1	8 − 6	4 − 4	11 − 8	3 − 2	15 − 9
13 − 8	7 − 4	10 − 7	0 − 0	12 − 8	5 − 5	4 − 3	8 − 7	7 − 3	7 − 6
5 − 3	7 − 5	2 − 1	6 − 6	8 − 4	2 − 2	13 − 6	15 − 8	2 − 0	13 − 9
1 − 1	11 − 9	10 − 4	9 − 2	14 − 6	8 − 0	9 − 4	10 − 2	6 − 5	8 − 3
7 − 7	14 − 8	12 − 9	9 − 8	12 − 7	9 − 9	15 − 7	8 − 8	14 − 9	9 − 7

9 × 9	3 × 5	8 × 5	2 × 6	4 × 7	0 × 3	7 × 2	1 × 5	7 × 8	4 × 0
3 × 4	5 × 9	0 × 2	7 × 3	4 × 1	2 × 7	6 × 3	5 × 4	1 × 0	9 × 2
1 × 1	9 × 0	2 × 8	6 × 4	0 × 7	8 × 1	3 × 3	4 × 8	9 × 3	2 × 0
4 × 9	7 × 0	1 × 2	8 × 4	6 × 5	2 × 9	9 × 4	0 × 1	7 × 4	5 × 8
0 × 8	4 × 2	9 × 8	3 × 6	5 × 5	1 × 6	5 × 0	6 × 6	2 × 1	7 × 9
9 × 1	2 × 2	5 × 1	4 × 3	0 × 0	8 × 9	3 × 7	9 × 7	1 × 7	6 × 0
5 × 6	7 × 5	3 × 0	8 × 8	1 × 3	8 × 3	5 × 2	0 × 4	9 × 5	6 × 7
2 × 3	8 × 6	0 × 5	6 × 1	3 × 8	7 × 6	1 × 8	9 × 6	4 × 4	5 × 3
7 × 7	1 × 4	6 × 2	4 × 5	2 × 4	8 × 0	3 × 1	6 × 8	0 × 9	8 × 7
3 × 2	4 × 6	1 × 9	5 × 7	8 × 2	0 × 6	7 × 1	2 × 5	6 × 9	3 × 9

MATH 87   by Hake and Saxon

5 × 6	4 × 3	9 × 8	7 × 5	2 × 9	8 × 4	9 × 3	6 × 9
9 × 4	2 × 5	7 × 6	4 × 8	7 × 9	5 × 4	3 × 2	9 × 7
3 × 7	8 × 5	6 × 2	5 × 5	3 × 5	2 × 4	7 × 7	8 × 9
6 × 4	2 × 8	4 × 4	8 × 2	3 × 9	6 × 6	9 × 9	5 × 3
4 × 6	8 × 8	5 × 7	6 × 3	2 × 2	7 × 4	3 × 8	8 × 6
2 × 6	5 × 9	3 × 3	9 × 2	6 × 7	4 × 5	7 × 2	9 × 6
5 × 2	7 × 8	2 × 3	6 × 8	4 × 7	9 × 5	3 × 6	8 × 7
3 × 4	7 × 3	5 × 8	4 × 2	8 × 3	2 × 7	6 × 5	4 × 9

$7\overline{)21}$	$2\overline{)10}$	$6\overline{)42}$	$1\overline{)3}$	$4\overline{)24}$	$3\overline{)6}$	$9\overline{)54}$	$6\overline{)18}$	$4\overline{)0}$	$5\overline{)30}$
$4\overline{)32}$	$8\overline{)56}$	$1\overline{)0}$	$6\overline{)12}$	$3\overline{)18}$	$9\overline{)72}$	$5\overline{)15}$	$2\overline{)8}$	$7\overline{)42}$	$6\overline{)36}$
$6\overline{)0}$	$5\overline{)10}$	$9\overline{)9}$	$2\overline{)6}$	$7\overline{)63}$	$4\overline{)16}$	$8\overline{)48}$	$1\overline{)2}$	$5\overline{)35}$	$3\overline{)21}$
$2\overline{)18}$	$6\overline{)6}$	$3\overline{)15}$	$8\overline{)40}$	$2\overline{)0}$	$5\overline{)20}$	$9\overline{)27}$	$1\overline{)8}$	$4\overline{)4}$	$7\overline{)35}$
$4\overline{)20}$	$9\overline{)63}$	$1\overline{)4}$	$7\overline{)14}$	$3\overline{)3}$	$8\overline{)24}$	$5\overline{)0}$	$6\overline{)24}$	$8\overline{)8}$	$2\overline{)16}$
$5\overline{)5}$	$8\overline{)64}$	$3\overline{)0}$	$4\overline{)28}$	$7\overline{)49}$	$2\overline{)4}$	$9\overline{)81}$	$3\overline{)12}$	$6\overline{)30}$	$1\overline{)5}$
$8\overline{)32}$	$1\overline{)1}$	$9\overline{)36}$	$3\overline{)27}$	$2\overline{)14}$	$5\overline{)25}$	$6\overline{)48}$	$8\overline{)0}$	$7\overline{)28}$	$4\overline{)36}$
$2\overline{)12}$	$5\overline{)45}$	$1\overline{)7}$	$4\overline{)8}$	$7\overline{)0}$	$8\overline{)16}$	$3\overline{)24}$	$9\overline{)45}$	$1\overline{)9}$	$6\overline{)54}$
$7\overline{)56}$	$9\overline{)0}$	$8\overline{)72}$	$2\overline{)2}$	$5\overline{)40}$	$3\overline{)9}$	$9\overline{)18}$	$1\overline{)6}$	$4\overline{)12}$	$7\overline{)7}$

$\dfrac{12}{5} =$	$\dfrac{7}{2} =$	$\dfrac{20}{3} =$	$\dfrac{5}{2} =$	$\dfrac{24}{12} =$
$\dfrac{10}{2} =$	$\dfrac{25}{6} =$	$\dfrac{5}{4} =$	$\dfrac{21}{8} =$	$\dfrac{6}{3} =$
$\dfrac{10}{5} =$	$\dfrac{21}{10} =$	$\dfrac{12}{12} =$	$\dfrac{15}{3} =$	$\dfrac{10}{3} =$
$\dfrac{16}{16} =$	$\dfrac{5}{3} =$	$\dfrac{27}{10} =$	$\dfrac{3}{2} =$	$\dfrac{11}{8} =$
$\dfrac{36}{12} =$	$\dfrac{11}{10} =$	$\dfrac{21}{16} =$	$\dfrac{4}{4} =$	$\dfrac{25}{9} =$
$\dfrac{11}{6} =$	$\dfrac{8}{8} =$	$\dfrac{20}{9} =$	$\dfrac{15}{2} =$	$\dfrac{4}{3} =$
$\dfrac{25}{8} =$	$\dfrac{15}{4} =$	$\dfrac{2}{2} =$	$\dfrac{25}{12} =$	$\dfrac{32}{16} =$
$\dfrac{8}{3} =$	$\dfrac{12}{4} =$	$\dfrac{25}{16} =$	$\dfrac{8}{5} =$	$\dfrac{27}{8} =$
$\dfrac{33}{20} =$	$\dfrac{4}{2} =$	$\dfrac{10}{9} =$	$\dfrac{24}{8} =$	$\dfrac{3}{3} =$
$\dfrac{9}{4} =$	$\dfrac{10}{10} =$	$\dfrac{15}{8} =$	$\dfrac{16}{3} =$	$\dfrac{33}{10} =$

$\frac{4}{20} =$	$\frac{2}{4} =$	$\frac{4}{12} =$	$\frac{6}{9} =$	$\frac{4}{8} =$
$\frac{4}{10} =$	$\frac{2}{16} =$	$\frac{10}{15} =$	$\frac{2}{8} =$	$\frac{10}{12} =$
$\frac{8}{12} =$	$\frac{2}{20} =$	$\frac{2}{6} =$	$\frac{6}{10} =$	$\frac{12}{24} =$
$\frac{14}{16} =$	$\frac{6}{12} =$	$\frac{10}{100} =$	$\frac{3}{15} =$	$\frac{6}{8} =$
$\frac{3}{6} =$	$\frac{10}{20} =$	$\frac{3}{12} =$	$\frac{3}{9} =$	$\frac{4}{16} =$
$\frac{8}{10} =$	$\frac{16}{32} =$	$\frac{4}{6} =$	$\frac{8}{16} =$	$\frac{5}{20} =$
$\frac{50}{100} =$	$\frac{2}{10} =$	$\frac{5}{15} =$	$\frac{9}{12} =$	$\frac{10}{16} =$
$\frac{2}{12} =$	$\frac{12}{16} =$	$\frac{7}{14} =$	$\frac{5}{10} =$	$\frac{4}{32} =$

$\dfrac{12}{16} =$	$\dfrac{16}{24} =$	$\dfrac{20}{6} =$	$\dfrac{6}{21} =$	$\dfrac{14}{8} =$
$\dfrac{18}{24} =$	$\dfrac{15}{6} =$	$\dfrac{6}{8} =$	$\dfrac{8}{3} =$	$\dfrac{5}{10} =$
$\dfrac{25}{12} =$	$\dfrac{24}{9} =$	$\dfrac{16}{20} =$	$\dfrac{18}{8} =$	$\dfrac{15}{24} =$
$\dfrac{8}{6} =$	$\dfrac{9}{6} =$	$\dfrac{10}{4} =$	$\dfrac{25}{100} =$	$\dfrac{6}{4} =$
$\dfrac{8}{24} =$	$\dfrac{10}{8} =$	$\dfrac{20}{6} =$	$\dfrac{20}{16} =$	$\dfrac{15}{20} =$
$\dfrac{16}{16} =$	$\dfrac{25}{10} =$	$\dfrac{21}{6} =$	$\dfrac{8}{12} =$	$\dfrac{12}{8} =$
$\dfrac{8}{12} =$	$\dfrac{12}{9} =$	$\dfrac{16}{32} =$	$\dfrac{20}{9} =$	$\dfrac{10}{3} =$
$\dfrac{20}{8} =$	$\dfrac{10}{6} =$	$\dfrac{12}{20} =$	$\dfrac{18}{12} =$	$\dfrac{12}{10} =$

MATH 87   by Hake and Saxon

$\dfrac{1}{5} =$	$\dfrac{3}{10} =$	$\dfrac{1}{4} =$	$\dfrac{1}{20} =$
$\dfrac{1}{8} =$	$\dfrac{1}{3} =$	$\dfrac{9}{10} =$	$\dfrac{7}{8} =$
$\dfrac{3}{5} =$	$\dfrac{1}{6} =$	$\dfrac{1}{2} =$	$\dfrac{1}{100} =$
$\dfrac{1}{50} =$	$\dfrac{5}{8} =$	$\dfrac{7}{10} =$	$\dfrac{3}{4} =$
$\dfrac{1}{25} =$	$\dfrac{2}{3} =$	$\dfrac{2}{5} =$	$\dfrac{5}{6} =$
$\dfrac{3}{8} =$	$\dfrac{4}{5} =$	$\dfrac{1}{10} =$	$\dfrac{1}{1000} =$

1% =	20% =	55% =	90% =	75% =
99% =	5% =	95% =	80% =	12% =
70% =	65% =	50% =	2% =	48% =
24% =	25% =	$33\frac{1}{3}\%$ =	40% =	15% =
60% =	30% =	4% =	35% =	36% =
45% =	8% =	10% =	$66\frac{2}{3}\%$ =	85% =

Fraction	Decimal	Percent
$\frac{1}{100}$		
$\frac{1}{50}$		
$\frac{1}{4}$		
$\frac{1}{8}$		
$\frac{1}{20}$		
$\frac{1}{3}$		
$\frac{7}{10}$		
$\frac{2}{5}$		
$\frac{1}{6}$		
$\frac{3}{8}$		
$\frac{1}{2}$		
$\frac{1}{10}$		
$\frac{1}{5}$		
$\frac{1}{1000}$		
$\frac{1}{12}$		
$\frac{2}{3}$		
$\frac{5}{8}$		
$\frac{4}{5}$		
$\frac{5}{6}$		
$\frac{3}{10}$		
$\frac{3}{4}$		
$\frac{7}{8}$		
$\frac{9}{10}$		
$\frac{3}{5}$		
$\frac{1}{25}$		

Math 87
Test Masters

Test Forms

Instructions

Tests are an important component of the Saxon program. We believe that concepts and skills should be continually tested. However, tests should only be administered after the concepts and skills have been thoroughly practiced. Therefore, we recommend that tests be administered according to the testing schedule which is printed on the back side of this page.

Note: Optional student answer forms are located at the back of this booklet. These forms provide sufficient writing space so that students can show all of their work along with their answers.

Math 87

Testing Schedule

Test to be administered:	Covers Material up through:	Give after teaching:
Test 1	Lesson 5	Lesson 10
Test 2	Lesson 10	Lesson 15
Test 3	Lesson 15	Lesson 20
Test 4	Lesson 20	Lesson 25
Test 5	Lesson 25	Lesson 30
Test 6	Lesson 30	Lesson 35
Test 7	Lesson 35	Lesson 40
Test 8	Lesson 40	Lesson 45
Test 9	Lesson 45	Lesson 50
Test 10	Lesson 50	Lesson 55
Test 11	Lesson 55	Lesson 60
Test 12	Lesson 60	Lesson 65
Test 13	Lesson 65	Lesson 70
Test 14	Lesson 70	Lesson 75
Test 15	Lesson 75	Lesson 80
Test 16	Lesson 80	Lesson 85
Test 17	Lesson 85	Lesson 90
Test 18	Lesson 90	Lesson 95
Test 19	Lesson 95	Lesson 100
Test 20	Lesson 100	Lesson 105
Test 21	Lesson 105	Lesson 110
Test 22	Lesson 110	Lesson 115
Test 23	Lesson 115	Lesson 120
Test 24	Lesson 120	Lesson 125
Test 25	Lesson 125	Lesson 130
Test 26	Lesson 130	Lesson 133
Test 27	Lesson 133	Lesson 133

1. If the product of 15 and 40 is divided by the sum of 15 and 45, what is the quotient?

2. List the whole numbers that are factors of 50.

3. Use digits and symbols to write "Negative seven is less than positive two."

4. Use words to write 21600050.

List the whole numbers from 1 to 10 that are divisors of:

5. 23

6. 73,500

7. Replace the circle with the proper comparison symbol.

$$-8 \bigcirc -11$$

8. Show this subtraction problem on a number line: $8 - 6$

9. Use digits to write eight million, one hundred thousand, sixty.

Find each missing number:

10.
$$\begin{array}{r} X \\ + \ \$4.30 \\ \hline \$15.00 \end{array}$$

11.
$$\begin{array}{r} Y \\ - \ 8860 \\ \hline 6300 \end{array}$$

12.
$$\begin{array}{r} Z \\ \times \quad 8 \\ \hline \$74.00 \end{array}$$

13.
$$\begin{array}{r} 1426 \\ - \quad A \\ \hline 78 \end{array}$$

14.
$$\begin{array}{r} 45 \\ \times \quad B \\ \hline 1575 \end{array}$$

15.
$$\begin{array}{r} 32,800 \\ - \quad C \\ \hline 9360 \end{array}$$

Add, subtract, multiply, or divide, as indicated:

16. $8 \cdot 12 \cdot 11$

17. $1000 - (560 - 79)$

18. $8 \overline{)46,392}$

19. $160(17)$

20. $\dfrac{\$29.80}{10}$

Math 87 by Hake & Saxon

1. If the product of 20 and 30 is divided by the sum of 20 and 30, what is the quotient?

2. List the whole numbers that are factors of 40.

3. Use digits and symbols to write "Negative three is less than positive two."

4. Use words to write 31020030.

List the whole numbers from 1 to 10 that are divisors of:

5. 29   6. 3500

7. Replace the circle with the proper comparison symbol.

$$-9 \bigcirc -10$$

8. Show this subtraction problem on a number line: $7 - 4$

9. Use digits to write twelve million, three hundred thousand, forty.

Find each missing number:

10.
$$\begin{array}{r} A \\ + \ \$3.40 \\ \hline \$15.00 \end{array}$$

11.
$$\begin{array}{r} B \\ - \ 5630 \\ \hline 7240 \end{array}$$

12.
$$\begin{array}{r} C \\ \times \quad 6 \\ \hline \$42.60 \end{array}$$

13.
$$\begin{array}{r} 35 \\ \times \quad D \\ \hline 770 \end{array}$$

14.
$$\begin{array}{r} 3714 \\ + \quad E \\ \hline 5860 \end{array}$$

15.
$$\begin{array}{r} 3400 \\ - \quad F \\ \hline 986 \end{array}$$

Add, subtract, multiply, or divide, as indicated:

16. $6 \cdot 12 \cdot 15$ 17. $1000 - (650 - 97)$

18. $9\overline{)46{,}306}$ 19. $150(16)$ 20. $\dfrac{\$76.50}{10}$

Math 87 by Hake & Saxon

1. As the day of the festival drew near, the city swelled to 300,000 occupants. If the usual population of the city was 73,000, how many visitors had come to the city?

2. Syd returned from the store with $15.73 after spending $86.09 on groceries. How much money did he have when he went to the store?

3. Exactly 10,000 participants began the gruelling marathon. If only 4520 participants finished the marathon, how many dropped out along the way?

4. Autumn was in the air. In the morning Ricky raked 1049 leaves. That afternoon he raked 2750 leaves. In all, how many leaves did Ricky rake that day?

5. Arrange these numbers in order from least to greatest:

    $$\frac{1}{3}, -3, 3, 0$$

6. Draw and shade circles to represent $1\frac{3}{4}$.

7. (a) What fraction of the rectangle is shaded?
    (b) What fraction of the rectangle is not shaded?

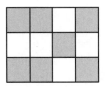

8. Subtract fifty-eight million from one hundred million and use words to write the difference.

9. (a) List the factors of 21.
    (b) List the factors of 48.
    (c) Which numbers are factors of both 21 and 48?

10. Use digits and symbols to write "The product of one and three is less than the sum of one and three."

Find each missing number:

11. $$\begin{array}{r} 2320 \\ + \quad M \\ \hline 4760 \end{array}$$

12. $$\begin{array}{r} N \\ - \$8.75 \\ \hline \$9.55 \end{array}$$

13. $$\begin{array}{r} 35 \\ \times \quad P \\ \hline 910 \end{array}$$

Add, subtract, multiply, or divide, as indicated:

14. $\frac{3}{5} + \frac{1}{5}$

15. $\frac{9}{11} - \frac{3}{11}$

16. $\frac{3}{5} \times \frac{4}{7}$

17. $9\overline{)74,309}$

18. $40(\$1.63)$

19. $\frac{2}{5} \cdot \frac{2}{5} \cdot \frac{2}{5}$

20. Describe each figure as a line, ray, or segment. Then use a symbol and letters to name each figure.
    (a) M   C
    (b) P   M
    (c) F   H

1. As the day of the festival drew near, the city swelled to 400,000 occupants. If the usual population of the city was 187,000, how many visitors had come to the city?

2. Sarah returned from the store with $15.72 after spending $76.84 on groceries. How much money did she have when she went to the store?

3. Exactly 10,000 participants began the gruelling race. If only 5809 participants finished the race, how many dropped out along the way?

4. Autumn was in the air. In the morning Raul raked 2089 leaves. That afternoon he raked 1790 leaves. In all, how many leaves did Raul rake that day?

5. Arrange these numbers in order from least to greatest:

$$\frac{1}{2}, -2, 2, 0$$

6. Draw and shade circles to represent $2\frac{3}{4}$.

7. (a) What fraction of the square is shaded?
   (b) What fraction of the square is not shaded?

8. Subtract forty-seven million from one hundred million and use words to write the difference.

9. (a) List the factors of 27.
   (b) List the factors of 45.
   (c) Which numbers are factors of both 27 and 45?

10. Use digits and symbols to write "The product of two and three is greater than the sum of two and three."

Find each missing number:

11.
$$
\begin{array}{r}
5370 \\
+ \quad Q \\
\hline
6184
\end{array}
$$

12.
$$
\begin{array}{r}
R \\
- \$7.85 \\
\hline
\$9.50
\end{array}
$$

13.
$$
\begin{array}{r}
35 \\
\times \quad T \\
\hline
840
\end{array}
$$

Add, subtract, multiply, or divide, as indicated:

14. $\dfrac{3}{7} + \dfrac{2}{7}$

15. $\dfrac{8}{9} - \dfrac{4}{9}$

16. $\dfrac{2}{5} \times \dfrac{3}{7}$

17. $8\overline{)74,000}$

18. $40(\$1.75)$

19. $\dfrac{3}{4} \cdot \dfrac{1}{2} \cdot \dfrac{3}{5}$

20. Describe each figure as a line, ray, or segment. Then use a symbol and letters to name each figure.

   (a) A ●——● B

   (b)   ←●——●→ C D

   (c) G ●——●→ H

Math 87 by Hake & Saxon

1. In 1980 the population of Ashton was 96,212. By the 1990 census, the population had increased to 100,219. The population of Ashton in 1990 was how much greater than the population in 1980?

2. The beach balls arrived packed 15 in each case. If 80 cases were delivered, how many beach balls were there in all?

3. The product of 7 and 9 is how much greater than the sum of 7 and 9?

4. Sam spent $5.85 for the ticket, $2.75 for popcorn, and 60¢ for a drink. How much did he spend in all?

5. How many years were there from 1673 to 1699?

6. This sign is incorrect. Show two ways to correct this sign.

> *Yogurt*
> **0.75¢ per cup**

7. Draw shaded circles to show that $3\frac{1}{3} = \frac{10}{3}$.

8. Complete each equivalent fraction.

   (a) $\frac{3}{4} = \frac{?}{12}$ (b) $\frac{2}{3} = \frac{?}{12}$

9. Use words to write 860900330.

10. (a) List the factors of 21.
    (b) List the factors of 42.
    (c) What is the greatest number that is a factor of both 21 and 42?

11. Name 3 segments in this figure in order of length from shortest to longest.

12. What mixed number is represented by point *A* on this number line?

Add, subtract, multiply, or divide, as indicated:

13. $\frac{7}{11} + \frac{5}{11}$ 14. $\frac{2}{3} \cdot \frac{7}{4}$ 15. $7\overline{)15,409}$

16. $\frac{8840}{40}$ 17. $\begin{array}{r} 735 \\ \times\ 14 \\ \hline \end{array}$ 18. $(9 + 4)(3)$

Find each missing number:

19. $\begin{array}{r} Q \\ \times\ 15 \\ \hline 4500 \end{array}$ 20. $\begin{array}{r} \$20.00 \\ -\ \ \ \ R \\ \hline \$8.43 \end{array}$

Math 87 **by Hake & Saxon**

1. In 1980 the population of Dearfield was 27,312. By the 1990 census, the population had increased to 31,080. The population of Dearfield in 1990 was how much greater than the population in 1980?

2. The beach balls arrived packed 18 in each case. If 50 cases were delivered, how many beach balls were there in all?

3. The product of 7 and 6 is how much greater than the sum of 7 and 6?

4. Leticia spent $5.95 for the ticket, $1.75 for popcorn, and 90¢ for a drink. How much did she spend in all?

5. How many years were there from 1776 to 1789?

6. This sign is incorrect. Show two ways to correct this sign.

> *Grapes*
> **0.45¢ per lb.**

7. Draw shaded circles to show that $2\frac{1}{2} = \frac{5}{2}$.

8. Complete each equivalent fraction.

(a) $\frac{5}{6} = \frac{?}{12}$ (b) $\frac{1}{2} = \frac{?}{12}$

9. Use words to write 609003308.

10. (a) List the factors of 15.

    (b) List the factors of 30.

    (c) What is the greatest number that is a factor of both 15 and 30?

11. Name 3 segments in this figure in order of length from shortest to longest.

12. What mixed number is represented by point B on this number line?

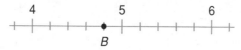

Add, subtract, multiply, or divide, as indicated:

13. $\frac{5}{7} + \frac{3}{7}$ 14. $\frac{3}{4} \cdot \frac{11}{6}$ 15. $\frac{18,036}{9}$

16. $30\overline{)8880}$ 17. $\begin{array}{r} 635 \\ \times\ 14 \\ \hline \end{array}$ 18. $(6 + 5)(4)$

Find each missing number:

19. $\begin{array}{r} T \\ \times\ 12 \\ \hline 4500 \end{array}$ 20. $\begin{array}{r} \$20.00 \\ -\quad V \\ \hline \$4.83 \end{array}$

Math 87 by Hake & Saxon

1. Great Grandpa celebrated his sixty-fifth birthday in 1973. In what year was he born?

2. The farmer harvested 8000 bushels of grain from 50 acres. The crop produced an average of how many bushels of grain for each acre?

3. One twelfth of the students in the class were left-handed. What fraction of the students were not left-handed?

4. Five hundred sixty-eight ducks floated peacefully on the lake. As the first shot rang out, all but 39 of the ducks flew away. How many ducks flew away?

5. Forty-seven million is how much less than one billion? Use words to write the answer.

6. Use words to write 278304011050.

7. Use digits and symbols to write "Seven minus nine equals negative two."

8. Find the perimeter of this rectangle.

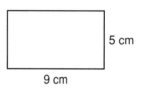

5 cm

9 cm

9. Reduce each fraction or mixed number.

    (a) $3\dfrac{24}{36}$

    (b) $\dfrac{9}{21}$

10. Write $\dfrac{8}{3}$ as a mixed number.

11. For each of these fractions, find an equivalent fraction that has a denominator of 36.

    (a) $\dfrac{3}{4} = \dfrac{?}{36}$

    (b) $\dfrac{4}{9} = \dfrac{?}{36}$

12. What kind of angle is every angle of a rectangle?

Find each missing number:

13.
$$
\begin{array}{r}
7937 \\
-\ \ \ G \\
\hline
1169
\end{array}
$$

14.
$$
\begin{array}{r}
H \\
\times\ \ \ 30 \\
\hline
\$41.10
\end{array}
$$

15. Which of the following does not equal $2\dfrac{2}{3}$?

    A. $\dfrac{11}{3}$

    B. $2\dfrac{4}{6}$

    C. $\dfrac{8}{3}$

    D. $2\dfrac{10}{15}$

Add, subtract, multiply, or divide, as indicated:

16. $\dfrac{3}{4} + \dfrac{3}{4} + \dfrac{3}{4}$

17. $\dfrac{9}{11} - \dfrac{7}{11}$

18. $\dfrac{3}{5} \cdot \dfrac{5}{6}$

19. $6\overline{)43{,}263}$

20. $13(11 + 13)$

Math 87 by Hake & Saxon

1. Great Grandma celebrated her seventy-fifth birthday in 1982. In what year was she born?

2. The farmer harvested 7000 bushels of grain from 50 acres. The crop produced an average of how many bushels of grain for each acre?

3. One eighth of the students in the class were left-handed. What fraction of the students were not left-handed?

4. Five hundred eighty-six ducks floated peacefully on the lake. As the first shot rang out, all but 39 of the ducks flew away. How many ducks flew away?

5. Seventy-four million is how much less than one billion? Use words to write the answer.

6. Use words to write 8304011050.

7. Use digits and symbols to write "Seven minus ten equals negative three."

8. Find the perimeter of this rectangle.

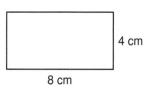

8 cm

9. Reduce each fraction or mixed number.

    (a) $5\dfrac{18}{24}$ (b) $\dfrac{12}{21}$

10. Write $\dfrac{10}{3}$ as a mixed number.

11. For each of these fractions, find an equivalent fraction that has a denominator of 36.

    (a) $\dfrac{5}{6} = \dfrac{?}{36}$ (b) $\dfrac{5}{9} = \dfrac{?}{36}$

12. What kind of angle is every angle of a rectangle?

Find each missing number:

13. $\begin{array}{r} 3797 \\ -\quad K \\ \hline 1169 \end{array}$

14. $\begin{array}{r} M \\ \times\quad 30 \\ \hline \$40.20 \end{array}$

15. Which of the following does not equal $2\dfrac{1}{4}$?

    A. $\dfrac{9}{4}$ B. $2\dfrac{2}{8}$ C. $\dfrac{7}{4}$ D. $\dfrac{18}{8}$

Add, subtract, multiply, or divide, as indicated:

16. $\dfrac{3}{5} + \dfrac{3}{5} + \dfrac{3}{5}$ 17. $\dfrac{9}{10} - \dfrac{7}{10}$ 18. $\dfrac{4}{5} \cdot \dfrac{5}{6}$

19. $7\overline{)43,463}$ 20. $12(11 + 13)$

1. At 1:00 p.m. there were 97 students in the cafeteria, 174 students on the playground, 17 students in the hallways, and 387 students in classrooms. How many students were there in all?

2. Marlin had 3200 postage stamps which he kept in envelopes. If each envelope contained 25 stamps, how many envelopes of stamps did he have?

3. Three hundred fifty-two million is how much less than two billion? Write the answer in words.

4. Marlin was carefully sorting his stamps when the wind whipped up. Of the 1025 stamps on the table before the wind whipped up, only 187 remained. How many stamps did the wind blow off the table?

5. Draw a diagram of this statement. Then answer the questions that follow.

    Three fifths of the 200 spectators roared with laughter at the clown's antics, while the rest of the spectators were mildly amused.

    (a) How many spectators roared with laughter?
    (b) How many spectators were mildly amused?

6. Simplify $\dfrac{22}{6}$ to a reduced mixed number.

7. Write $4\dfrac{2}{3}$ as an improper fraction.

8. Write the prime factorization of 480.

9. For each fraction, write an equivalent fraction that has a denominator of 60.

    (a) $\dfrac{1}{6}$ (b) $\dfrac{2}{5}$

Refer to rectangle *ABCD* to answer questions 10 and 11.
10. What side of the rectangle is parallel to side *BC*?

11. If *AB* is 25 mm and *BC* is 15 mm, what is the perimeter of the rectangle?

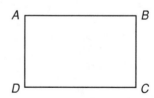

Solve:

12. $63 + m = 129$ 13. $x - 49 = 34$

14. $56 - w = 33$ 15. $7y = 91$

Add, subtract, multiply, or divide, as indicated:

16. $\dfrac{3}{4} + \dfrac{3}{4} + \dfrac{3}{4}$ 17. $\dfrac{7}{12} - \dfrac{5}{12}$ 18. $\dfrac{9}{2} \cdot \dfrac{8}{3}$

19. $\begin{array}{r} \$12.75 \\ \times \quad 16 \\ \hline \end{array}$ 20. $\dfrac{6000}{16}$

Math 87 by Hake & Saxon

1. At noon there were 156 students in the cafeteria, 117 students on the playground, 19 students in the hallway, and 174 students in classrooms. How many students were there in all?

2. Marlene had 2400 pennies that she was putting into rolls. If each roll held 50 pennies, how many rolls of pennies could she make?

3. Three hundred sixty-two million is how much less than two billion? Write the answer in words.

4. Thirty-seven thousand, five hundred scurried through the colony before the edentate attacked. Afterward only nine thousand, seven hundred remained. How many were lost when the edentate attacked?

5. Draw a diagram of this statement. Then answer the questions that follow.

   Three fifths of the 250 spectators roared with laughter at the clown's antics, while the rest of the spectators were mildly amused.

   (a) How many spectators roared with laughter?
   (b) How many spectators were mildly amused?

6. Simplify $\dfrac{21}{6}$ to a reduced mixed number.

7. Write $5\dfrac{1}{3}$ as an improper fraction.

8. Write the prime factorization of 490.

9. For each fraction, write an equivalent fraction that has a denominator of 60.

   (a) $\dfrac{1}{4}$ (b) $\dfrac{4}{5}$

Refer to rectangle *ABCD* to answer questions 10 and 11.
10. What side of the rectangle is parallel to side *CD*?

11. If *AB* is 20 mm and *BC* is 15 mm, what is the perimeter of the rectangle?

Solve:
12. $36 + m = 129$

13. $x - 34 = 48$

14. $65 - w = 33$

15. $6y = 96$

Add, subtract, multiply, or divide, as indicated:

16. $\dfrac{3}{5} + \dfrac{3}{5} + \dfrac{3}{5}$ 17. $\dfrac{7}{10} - \dfrac{3}{10}$ 18. $\dfrac{9}{4} \cdot \dfrac{8}{3}$

19. $\$12.75 \times 12$ 20. $\dfrac{6000}{80}$

Math 87 by Hake & Saxon

1. Six hundred twenty-four books were packed into 26 boxes. If each box contained the same number of books, how many books were packed in each box?

2. The Holy Roman Empire lasted from 962 to 1806. How many years did the Holy Roman Empire last?

3. Jan went to the ball game with $20.00 and returned with $9.30. How much money did Jan spend at the ball game?

4. Tom was engrossed in his 340-page book. He stopped on page 127 at noon to eat lunch. He stopped on page 253 to eat dinner. How many pages did Tom read during the afternoon?

5. Draw a diagram of this statement. Then answer the questions that follow.

    Three eighths of the 64 marbles in the bag were blue.

    (a) How many of the marbles in the bag were blue?
    (b) How many of the marbles in the bag were not blue?

6. (a) What fraction of this square is shaded?
    (b) What fraction of this square is not shaded?

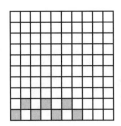

7. Simplify each fraction or mixed number.

    (a) $\dfrac{108}{8}$ (b) $8\dfrac{8}{6}$ (c) $\dfrac{120}{900}$

8. Write the reciprocal of each of these numbers.

    (a) $\dfrac{4}{9}$ (b) $6\dfrac{3}{4}$ (c) 9

9. Complete each equivalent fraction.

    (a) $\dfrac{5}{8} = \dfrac{?}{48}$ (b) $\dfrac{7}{16} = \dfrac{?}{48}$

Solve:

10. $350 = 700 - x$ 11. $y - 48 = 25$ 12. $12w = 264$

Add, subtract, multiply, or divide, as indicated:

13. $7 - 1\dfrac{5}{6}$ 14. $5\dfrac{4}{5} + 6\dfrac{3}{5}$ 15. $5\dfrac{1}{8} - 1\dfrac{7}{8}$

16. $3\dfrac{1}{3} \cdot 2\dfrac{2}{5}$ 17. $3\dfrac{3}{4} \div 4\dfrac{1}{2}$ 18. $2\dfrac{2}{3} \cdot 4$

19. $\dfrac{3}{4} \cdot \dfrac{5}{6} \cdot \dfrac{8}{15}$ 20. $3\dfrac{2}{3} \div 4$

Math 87 by Hake & Saxon

1. Six hundred twenty-four books were packed into 24 boxes. If each box contained the same number of books, how many books were packed in each box?

2. How many years were there from 864 to 1509?

3. Jerry went to the ball game with $20.00 and returned with $7.30. How much money did Jerry spend at the ball game?

4. Tom was enjoying his 360-page book. He stopped on page 137 at noon to eat lunch. He stopped on page 223 to eat dinner. How many pages did Tom read during the afternoon?

5. Draw a diagram of this statement. Then answer the questions that follow.

   One fourth of the 64 marbles in the bag were red.

   (a) How many of the marbles in the bag were red?
   (b) How many of the marbles in the bag were not red?

6. (a) What fraction of this square is shaded?
   (b) What fraction of this square is not shaded?

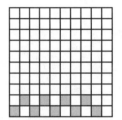

7. Simplify each fraction or mixed number.

   (a) $\dfrac{66}{9}$ (b) $6\dfrac{6}{9}$ (c) $\dfrac{660}{900}$

8. Write the reciprocal of each of these numbers.

   (a) $\dfrac{5}{8}$ (b) $3\dfrac{3}{5}$ (c) 3

9. Complete each equivalent fraction.

   (a) $\dfrac{5}{8} = \dfrac{?}{24}$ (b) $\dfrac{5}{12} = \dfrac{?}{24}$

Solve:

10. $250 = 600 - x$ 11. $y - 25 = 46$ 12. $12w = 276$

Add, subtract, multiply, or divide, as indicated:

13. $6 - 1\dfrac{1}{6}$ 14. $5\dfrac{4}{5} + 3\dfrac{4}{5}$ 15. $3\dfrac{1}{8} - 1\dfrac{3}{8}$

16. $3\dfrac{1}{3} \cdot 1\dfrac{4}{5}$ 17. $3\dfrac{1}{3} \div 4\dfrac{1}{6}$ 18. $2\dfrac{1}{4} \cdot 3$

19. $\dfrac{5}{6} \cdot \dfrac{4}{3} \cdot \dfrac{9}{20}$ 20. $2\dfrac{1}{4} \div 3$

Math 87 by Hake & Saxon

1. The 5 starters on the basketball team were tall. Their heights were 70 inches, 71 inches, 72 inches, 73 inches, and 84 inches. What was the average height of the 5 starters?

2. Marie bought 8 pounds of apples for $0.82 per pound and paid for them with a ten-dollar bill. How much should she get back in change?

3. On the first day of their 2598-mile trip, the Curtis family drove 683 miles. How many more miles do they have to drive until they complete their trip?

4. One hundred six of the two hundred sixty-three students in the auditorium were boys. How many girls were in the auditorium?

5. Draw a diagram of this statement. Then answer the questions that follow.

   The Daltons completed two sevenths of their 2170-mile trip the first day.

   (a) How many miles did they travel the first day?
   (b) How many miles of their trip do they still have to travel?

6. If the perimeter of a square is 3 feet, how many inches long is each side of the square?

7. Rewrite $\dfrac{2}{5}$ and $\dfrac{3}{4}$ so that they have common denominators.

8. (a) Round 44,283 to the nearest thousand.
   (b) Round 44,283 to the nearest hundred.

9. Estimate the quotient when 29,376 is divided by 29.

10. Simplify: $\dfrac{90}{20}$

11. Replace the circle with the proper comparison symbol.

   $$\frac{3}{5} \bigcirc \frac{5}{3}$$

12. Find the least common multiple (LCM) of 8 and 12.

13. Write the prime factorization of 215.

14. What is the average of 5, 4, 9, 11, 12, 13, 25, 26, and 30?

Solve:

15. $7w = 4 \cdot 21$ 16. $417 + a = 653$ 17. $91 - d = 42$

Add, subtract, multiply, or divide, as indicated:

18. $\dfrac{1}{4} + \dfrac{1}{3}$ 19. $\left(\dfrac{3}{4} \cdot \dfrac{1}{3}\right) - \dfrac{1}{6}$ 20. $1\dfrac{3}{5} \div 2\dfrac{1}{2}$

Math 87 by Hake & Saxon

1. The 5 starters on the basketball team were tall. Their heights were 71 inches, 72 inches, 73 inches, 75 inches, and 84 inches. What was the average height of the 5 starters?

2. Miguel bought 7 pounds of apples for $0.78 per pound and paid for them with a ten-dollar bill. How much should he get back in change?

3. On the first day of their 2058-mile trip, the Martins drove 586 miles. How many more miles do they have to drive until they complete their trip?

4. One hundred forty of the two hundred sixty-three students in the auditorium were girls. How many boys were in the auditorium?

5. Draw a diagram of this statement. Then answer the questions that follow.

    The Claytons completed two sevenths of their 2030-mile trip the first day.

    (a) How many miles did they travel the first day?
    (b) How many miles of their trip do they still have to travel?

6. If the perimeter of a square is 5 feet, how many inches long is each side of the square?

7. Rewrite $\frac{3}{5}$ and $\frac{1}{4}$ so that they have common denominators.

8. (a) Round 42,846 to the nearest thousand.
    (b) Round 42,846 to the nearest hundred.

9. Estimate the quotient when 20,260 is divided by 19.

10. Simplify: $\frac{90}{40}$

11. Replace the circle with the proper comparison symbol.

    $$\frac{3}{4} \bigcirc \frac{4}{3}$$

12. Find the least common multiple (LCM) of 10 and 12.

13. Write the prime factorization of 220.

14. What is the average of 6, 5, 10, 12, 13, 14, 26, 27, and 31?

Solve:

15. $7w = 5 \cdot 14$ 16. $516 + m = 653$ 17. $81 - f = 42$

Add, subtract, multiply, or divide, as indicated:

18. $\frac{3}{4} - \frac{1}{3}$ 19. $\left(\frac{1}{4} \cdot \frac{2}{3} \right) - \frac{1}{6}$ 20. $2\frac{1}{2} \div 1\frac{3}{5}$

Math 87 by Hake & Saxon

1. In the first four months of the year the Montgomerys' electric bills were $120.46, $134.59, $118.38, and $96.29. What was their average electricity bill during the first four months of the year?

2. The price was reduced from four thousand, four hundred ninety-six dollars to one thousand, eight hundred ninety-three dollars. By how much was the price reduced?

3. A one-year subscription to the monthly magazine costs $15.60. The regular newsstand price is $1.95 per issue. How much is saved per issue by paying the subscription price?

4. Carlos ran one lap in one minute seven seconds. Orlando ran one lap six seconds faster than Carlos. How many seconds did it take Orlando to run one lap?

5. The perimeter of the square equals the perimeter of the regular pentagon. Each side of the pentagon is 16 cm. How long is each side of the square?

6. Draw a diagram of this statement. Then answer the questions that follow.

    Four ninths of the 63 fish in the tank were guppies.

    (a) How many of the fish were guppies?

    (b) How many of the fish were not guppies?

7. Find the least common multiple (LCM) of 7, 9, and 21.

8. Round 3849.4151

    (a) to the nearest hundredth.   (b) to the nearest hundred.

9. (a) What fraction of this square is not shaded?

    (b) What decimal part of this square is not shaded?

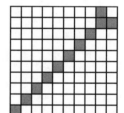

10. Use words to write 100.113.

11. Use digits to write eighty-five hundred-thousandths.

12. What decimal number names the point marked with an arrow on this number line?

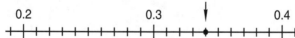

13. Simplify: $\dfrac{363}{36}$

14. What decimal number is halfway between 14 and 15?

Solve:

15. $18x = 9 \cdot 10$

16. $708 - y = 512$

Add, subtract, multiply, or divide, as indicated:

17. $4.3 + 1.79 + 11$

18. $42.61 - 3.095$

19. $1\dfrac{1}{5} - \left(\dfrac{1}{4} \cdot \dfrac{2}{5} \right)$

20. $\left(2\dfrac{1}{4} + 1\dfrac{1}{3} \right) \div \left(2 - 1\dfrac{1}{6} \right)$

Math 87 **by Hake & Saxon**

1. In the first four months of the year Gerardo's electric bills were $115.46, $129.59, $113.38, and $91.29. What was Gerardo's average electricity bill for the four months?

2. The price was reduced from one thousand, two hundred ninety-six dollars to nine hundred ninety-eight dollars. By how much was the price reduced?

3. A one-year subscription to the monthly magazine costs $14.88. The regular newsstand price is $1.95 per issue. How much is saved per issue by paying the subscription price?

4. Jimmy ran one lap in one minute six seconds. Braulio ran one lap four seconds faster than Jimmy. How many seconds did it take Braulio to run one lap?

5. The perimeter of the square equals the perimeter of the regular pentagon. Each side of the square is 15 cm. How long is each side of the pentagon?

6. Draw a diagram of this statement. Then answer the questions that follow.

    Four sevenths of the 63 fish in the tank were guppies.

    (a) How many of the fish were guppies?

    (b) How many of the fish were not guppies?

7. Find the least common multiple (LCM) of 7, 9, and 14.

8. Round 3849.4151

    (a) to the nearest tenth.   (b) to the nearest ten.

9. (a) What fraction of this square is shaded?
   (b) What decimal part of this square is shaded?

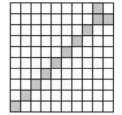

10. Use words to write 100.13.

11. Use digits to write fifty-eight hundred-thousandths.

12. What decimal number names the point marked with an arrow on this number line?

13. Simplify: $\dfrac{124}{12}$

14. What decimal number is halfway between 16 and 17?

Solve:

15. $16x = 8 \cdot 10$ 16. $807 - y = 512$

Add, subtract, multiply, or divide, as indicated:

17. $3.4 + 1.78 + 12$ 18. $21.62 - 3.083$

19. $1\dfrac{2}{5} - \left(\dfrac{3}{4} \cdot \dfrac{1}{5}\right)$ 20. $\left(2\dfrac{1}{4} - 1\dfrac{1}{3}\right) \div \left(2 + 1\dfrac{1}{6}\right)$

Math 87 by Hake & Saxon

1. The bag contained only red marbles and white marbles. If the ratio of red marbles to white marbles was 5 to 4, what fraction of the marbles were white?

2. John ran 4 laps of the track in 5 minutes 40 seconds.
    (a) How many seconds did it take John to run 4 laps?
    (b) John's average time for running each lap was how many seconds?

3. The Curtis's car traveled an average of 21 miles per gallon of gas. At that rate, how far could the car travel on a full tank of 21 gallons?

4. Draw a diagram of this statement. Then answer the questions that follow.
    Three fourths of the 104 adults in the McGlaughlin clan were 5 feet tall or taller.
    (a) How many of the adults were less than 5 feet tall?
    (b) How many of the adults were 5 feet tall or taller?

5. What is the perimeter of the polygon? Dimensions are in millimeters.

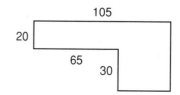

6. *AB* is 35 mm. *CD* is 45 mm. *AD* is 110 mm. Find *BC*.

7. The length of segment *CD* in problem 6 is 45 mm. What is the length of segment *CD* in centimeters?

8. Round 0.910346 to the nearest thousandth.

9. Use words to write 17.0703.

10. Use digits to write four billion, two hundred fifty million, eight hundred sixty thousand.

11. What decimal names point *C* on this number line?

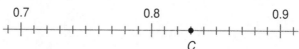

12. Write sixty-five and three hundredths
    (a) as a decimal.   (b) as a mixed number.

13. In this figure, which angle looks like
    (a) a right angle?
    (b) an obtuse angle?

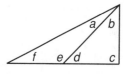

Add, subtract, multiply, or divide, as indicated:

14. $0.12(0.06)$

15. $3\frac{1}{2} + 4\frac{5}{7}$

16. $5\frac{1}{3} - 3\frac{5}{6}$

17. $8\frac{1}{4} \cdot 1\frac{7}{11}$

18. $5\frac{4}{9} \div 7$

Solve:

19. $\frac{8}{10} = \frac{w}{15}$

20. $m + 0.72 = 1.54$

1. The bag contained only red marbles and blue marbles. If the ratio of red marbles to blue marbles was 5 to 3, what fraction of the marbles were blue?

2. James ran 4 laps of the track in 6 minutes 20 seconds.

   (a) How many seconds did it take James to run 4 laps?

   (b) What was the average number of seconds it took James to run each lap?

3. Maria's car traveled an average of 24 miles per gallon of gas. At that rate, how far could her car travel on a full tank of 18 gallons?

4. Draw a diagram of this statement. Then answer the questions that follow.

   Four-fifths of the 105 adults in the McCoy clan were 5 feet tall or taller.

   (a) How many of the adults were less than 5 feet tall?

   (b) How many of the adults were 5 feet tall or taller?

5. What is the perimeter of the polygon? Dimensions are in millimeters.

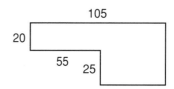

6. *AB* is 25 mm. *CD* is 45 mm. *AD* is 110 mm. Find *BC*.

7. The length of segment *AB* in problem 6 is 25 mm. What is the length of segment *AB* in centimeters?

8. Round 0.910463 to the nearest thousandth.

9. Use words to write 37.0701.

10. Use digits to write two billion, two hundred thirty million, five hundred eighty-six thousand.

11. What decimal names point *C* on this number line?

12. Write thirty-four and seven hundredths

    (a) as a decimal.   (b) as a mixed number.

13. In this figure, which angle looks like

    (a) a right angle?

    (b) an obtuse angle?

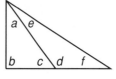

Add, subtract, multiply, or divide, as indicated:

14. $0.15(0.05)$ 15. $3\frac{1}{2} + 4\frac{2}{5}$ 16. $5\frac{2}{3} - 2\frac{5}{6}$

17. $6\frac{1}{4} \cdot 1\frac{3}{5}$ 18. $7 \div 5\frac{4}{9}$

Solve:

19. $\dfrac{6}{10} = \dfrac{w}{15}$ 20. $m + 0.27 = 1.54$

1. The rectangle was 21 inches long and 6 inches wide. What was the ratio of its width to its length?

2. Amber's test scores were 90, 91, 90, 87, 85, 95, 92, 80, 100, and 100. What was her average test score?

3. Fifty-four thousandths is how much less than forty-three hundredths?

Refer to this election tally sheet to answer questions 4 and 5.

4. The second-place candidate received how many more votes than the third-place candidate?

5. What fraction of the votes did Yolanda receive?

VOTE TOTALS

Judy	$\cancel{				}$ $\cancel{				}$ $\cancel{				}$ $	$
Carlos	$\cancel{				}$ $\cancel{				}$ $				$
Yolanda	$\cancel{				}$ $\cancel{				}$ $\cancel{				}$ $\cancel{				}$ $		$
Khanh	$\cancel{				}$ $\cancel{				}$ $\cancel{				}$ $			$

6. Draw a diagram of this statement. Then answer the questions that follow.

    Three eighths of those who rode the Giant Gyro at the fair were euphoric. All the rest were vertiginous.

    (a) What fraction of those who rode the ride were vertiginous?
    (b) What was the ratio of euphoric to vertiginous riders?

7. The perimeter of the rectangle is 68 cm. What is the length of the rectangle?

12 cm

8. Write 6.25 as a mixed number.

9. Write $\frac{9}{5}$ as a decimal.

10. Round $52.\overline{23}$ to five decimal places.

11. Divide 34 by 5 and write the answer as a decimal number.

12. Divide 4.3 by 9 and write the quotient with a bar over the repetend.

Solve:

13. $\frac{12}{8} = \frac{3}{m}$ 14. $7 = 3.14 + x$ 15. $0.091 = 1 - z$

Add, subtract, multiply, or divide, as indicated:

16. $5\frac{3}{5} + \frac{3}{4} + 2\frac{1}{2}$ 17. $3\frac{1}{4} - \left(3 - 1\frac{5}{6}\right)$ 18. $3\frac{3}{4} \cdot 3\frac{1}{5} \cdot 6$

19. $4 \div 10\frac{2}{3}$ 20. $2.5(0.4)(0.05)$

Math 87 **by Hake & Saxon**

1. The rectangle was 20 inches long and 8 inches wide. What was the ratio of its width to its length?

2. Eric's test scores were 90, 89, 88, 87, 83, 95, 90, 80, 98, and 100. What was his average test score?

3. Forty-five thousandths is how much less than forty-three hundredths?

Refer to this election tally sheet to answer questions 4 and 5.

4. The first-place candidate received how many more votes than the third-place candidate?

5. What fraction of the votes did Carlos receive?

VOTE TOTALS

Judy	॥H ॥H ॥H l
Carlos	॥H ॥H llll
Yolanda	॥H ॥H ॥H ॥H ll
Khanh	॥H ॥H ॥H lll

6. Draw a diagram of this statement. Then answer the questions that follow.

Four ninths of those who rode the Giant Gyro at the fair were euphoric. All the rest were vertiginous.

(a) What fraction of those who rode the ride were vertiginous?

(b) What was the ratio of euphoric to vertiginous riders?

7. The perimeter of the rectangle is 60 cm. What is the length of the rectangle?

8. Write 6.75 as a mixed number.

12 cm

9. Write $\dfrac{8}{5}$ as a decimal.

10. Round $15.\overline{54}$ to four decimal places.

11. Divide 33 by 5 and write the answer as a decimal number.

12. Divide 3.4 by 9 and write the quotient with a bar over the repetend.

Solve:

13. $\dfrac{12}{9} = \dfrac{8}{m}$ **14.** $6 = 3.14 + y$ **15.** $0.91 = 1 - x$

Add, subtract, multiply, or divide, as indicated:

16. $5\dfrac{2}{5} + \dfrac{3}{4} + 3\dfrac{1}{2}$ **17.** $5\dfrac{1}{4} - \left(3 - 1\dfrac{1}{6}\right)$ **18.** $3\dfrac{3}{4} \cdot 3\dfrac{3}{5} \cdot 6$

19. $10\dfrac{2}{3} \div 4$ **20.** $2.5(0.8)(0.05)$

Math 87 by Hake & Saxon

1. Alaska became a state in 1959. Alaska was purchased 92 years prior to becoming a state. In what year was Alaska purchased?

2. Brand X costs $1.56 for 12 ounces. Brand Y costs 2¢ more per ounce. What is the cost of 15 ounces of Brand Y?

3. The ratio of black beans to sweet peas in the garden was 12 to 5. What was the ratio of sweet peas to black beans?

4. During the month of February, Hal's weekly grocery bills were $109.60, $114.56, $85.90, and $122.14. Find his average weekly grocery bill in February to the nearest dollar.

5. Five and nine hundredths is how much less than nine? Write the answer in words.

6. Draw a diagram of this statement. Then answer the questions that follow.
   Seven eighths of the 72 buttons in the box had 5 holes.
   (a) What fraction of the buttons did not have 5 holes?
   (b) How many buttons did not have 5 holes?

7. Find the length of this segment
   (a) to the nearest centimeter.
   (b) to the nearest eighth of an inch.

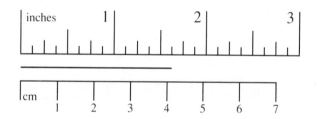

8. Write 0.24 as a reduced fraction.

9. Divide 4.8 by 11 and write the answer with a bar over the repetend.

10. Simplify: $\dfrac{490}{560}$

11. If the perimeter of a square is 32 inches, what is its area?

Solve:

12. $\dfrac{49}{56} = \dfrac{21}{f}$

13. $3w = 8.4$

14. $5 - m = 1.36$

Add, subtract, multiply, or divide, as indicated:

15. $8^2 - 3^3$

16. $\sqrt{64} - \sqrt{36}$

17. $14\dfrac{11}{12} - 8\dfrac{3}{8}$

18. $5\dfrac{3}{7} \div 3\dfrac{4}{5}$

19. 0.245×10^3

20. $0.1004 \div 0.08$

Math 87 by Hake & Saxon

1. What year was 284 years before 1776?

2. Brand X costs $1.65 for 11 ounces. Brand Y costs 2¢ more per ounce. What is the cost of 15 ounces of Brand Y?

3. The ratio of green beans to radishes in the garden was 5 to 2. What was the ratio of radishes to green beans?

4. During the month of February, George's weekly grocery bills were $107.60, $112.56, $83.90, and $120.14. Find his average weekly grocery bill in February to the nearest dollar.

5. Five and nine hundredths is how much less than five and nine tenths? Write the answer in words.

6. Draw a diagram of this statement. Then answer the questions that follow.
    Five sixths of the 72 buttons had 4 holes.
    (a) What fraction of the buttons did not have 4 holes?
    (b) How many buttons did not have 4 holes?

7. Find the length of this segment
    (a) to the nearest centimeter.
    (b) to the nearest eighth of an inch.

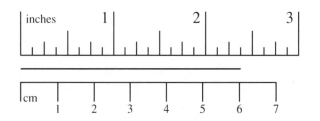

8. Write 0.28 as a reduced fraction.

9. Divide 4.9 by 11 and write the answer with a bar over the repetend.

10. Simplify: $\dfrac{560}{720}$

11. If the perimeter of a square is 28 inches, what is its area?

Solve:

12. $\dfrac{35}{55} = \dfrac{21}{f}$

13. $3w = 8.7$

14. $5 - n = 1.42$

Add, subtract, multiply, or divide, as indicated:

15. $8^2 - 4^3$

16. $\sqrt{49} - \sqrt{25}$

17. $12\dfrac{5}{8} - 8\dfrac{7}{12}$

18. $5\dfrac{1}{5} \div 2\dfrac{1}{6}$

19. 0.425×10^3

20. $1.008 \div 0.08$

1. At 23 miles per gallon, how far could a car travel on 15.1 gallons of gas?

2. Fifty-six and two hundred seven thousandths is how much less than one hundred five and three hundredths?

3. When twelve squared is divided by the square root of 9, what is the quotient?

4. Draw a diagram of this statement. Then answer the questions that follow.
    Five ninths of 4950 voters supported Mayor Roland.

    (a) How many voters did not support Mayor Roland?
    (b) What was the ratio of voters who supported the mayor to those who did not support the mayor?

5. What percent of the circle is shaded?

6. Write each percent as a reduced fraction or mixed number.
    (a) 18%   (b) 180%

7. Write each fraction or mixed number as a percent.

    (a) $3\dfrac{3}{4}$ (b) $\dfrac{1}{3}$

8. Change 70 inches to feet and inches.

9. Josephine bunted the ball and ran 90 feet to first base. How many yards did she run?

10. Divide 464 by 7 and write the answer as a mixed number.

Refer to this hexagon to answer questions 11 and 12.
Dimensions are in feet.

11. What is the perimeter of the hexagon?

12. What is the area of the hexagon?

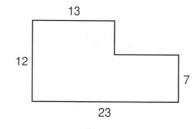

Solve:

13. $\dfrac{45}{50} = \dfrac{27}{k}$ 14. $x + 5.26 = 7$ 15. $m - \dfrac{5}{6} = \dfrac{1}{12}$

Add, subtract, multiply, or divide, as indicated:

16. $1^3 + 2^4 + 3^4 - \sqrt{49}$ 17. $0.04 \times 7.5 \times 10^4$

18. $\dfrac{27 \text{ miles}}{\text{hour}} \cdot 5 \text{ hours}$ 19. $\begin{array}{r} 4 \text{ yd } 1 \text{ ft } 8 \text{ in.} \\ + \qquad 2 \text{ ft } 5 \text{ in.} \\ \hline \end{array}$

20. $3\dfrac{1}{4} \div \left(2\dfrac{2}{5} \cdot 1\dfrac{1}{4}\right)$

1. At 24 miles per gallon, how far could a car travel on 14.1 gallons of gas?

2. Sixty-five and two hundred seventeen thousandths is how much less than one hundred twenty and five hundredths?

3. When ten squared is divided by the square root of 25, what is the quotient?

4. Draw a diagram of this statement. Then answer the questions that follow.
    Five eighths of the 4960 voters supported Mayor Rios.
    (a) How many voters did not support Mayor Rios?
    (b) What was the ratio of voters who supported the mayor to those who did not support the mayor?

5. What percent of the circle is not shaded?

6. Write each percent as a reduced fraction or mixed number.
    (a) 16%   (b) 160%

7. Write each fraction or mixed number as a percent.
    (a) $2\frac{3}{4}$ (b) $\frac{2}{3}$

8. Change 75 inches to feet and inches.

9. Nelson took the hand-off and ran 30 yards with the football. How many feet did he run?

10. Divide 360 by 7 and write the answer as a mixed number.

Refer to this hexagon to answer questions 11 and 12.
Dimensions are in centimeters.

11. What is the perimeter of the hexagon?

12. What is the area of the hexagon?

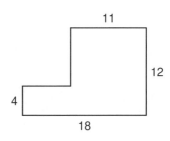

Solve:

13. $\dfrac{h}{10} = \dfrac{5}{4}$ 14. $x + 6.52 = 7$ 15. $m - \dfrac{3}{4} = \dfrac{1}{12}$

Add, subtract, multiply, or divide, as indicated:

16. $1^4 + 2^3 + 3^2 + 4^1 - \sqrt{25}$ 17. $0.02 \times 2.5 \times 10^4$

18. $\dfrac{27 \text{ miles}}{\text{gallon}} \cdot 14 \text{ gallons}$

19. $\begin{array}{r} 4 \text{ days } 17 \text{ hr } 13 \text{ min} \\ + \qquad\quad 18 \text{ hr } 50 \text{ min} \\ \hline \end{array}$

20. $2\dfrac{2}{3} \div \left(3\dfrac{1}{5} \cdot 1\dfrac{2}{3}\right)$

Math 87 by Hake & Saxon

1. The ratio of schooners to skiffs in the bay was 7 to 5. If there were 63 schooners in the bay, how many skiffs were there?

2. The average of four numbers is 98. If three of the numbers are 86, 87, and 91, what is the fourth number?

3. A one-quart container of milk costs 73¢. A case of 12 one-quart containers costs $7.68. How much is saved per quart by buying the milk by the case?

4. Segment *AB* is how much longer than segment *BC*?

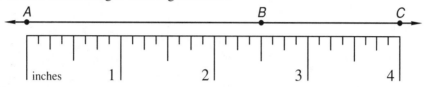

5. Draw a diagram of this statement. Then answer the questions that follow.

    Three tenths of the 40 students earned an A.

    (a) How many students earned an A?

    (b) What percent of the students earned an A?

6. Write forty billion in scientific notation.

7. Write 1.86×10^7 in standard form.

8. Use a unit multiplier to convert 800 mm to cm.

9. Write 410% as a mixed number.

10. Don is 5 feet 11 inches tall. Bob is 68 inches tall. Don is how many inches taller than Bob?

Refer to this figure to answer questions 11 and 12.
Dimensions are in inches.

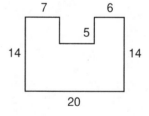

11. What is the area of the figure?

12. What is the perimeter of the figure?

Solve:

13. $5.64 + w = 10$

14. $\dfrac{a}{8} = \dfrac{45}{10}$

Add, subtract, multiply, or divide, as indicated:

15. $13^2 - 2^5 - 3^3 - \sqrt{169}$

16.
$$\begin{array}{r} 8 \text{ yd } 2 \text{ ft } 9 \text{ in.} \\ + \qquad 2 \text{ ft } 5 \text{ in.} \\ \hline \end{array}$$

17. $2\dfrac{1}{4} + 2\dfrac{5}{6} + 3\dfrac{5}{8}$

18. $6\dfrac{2}{3} \cdot 5\dfrac{1}{4} \cdot 2\dfrac{1}{10}$

19. $0.4(0.25)(0.01)$

20. $4.8 \div 0.016$

Math 87 by Hake & Saxon

1. The ratio of sailboats to dinghies in the bay was 5 to 7. If there were 70 sailboats in the bay, how many dinghies were there?

2. The average of four numbers is 97. If three of the numbers are 87, 91, and 99, what is the fourth number?

3. A liter of milk costs 68¢. A case of 12 liters of milk costs $7.56. How much is saved per liter by buying the milk by the case?

4. Segment *AB* is how much longer than segment *BC*?

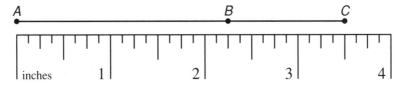

5. Draw a diagram of this statement. Then answer the questions that follow.

     Two fifths of the 40 students earned an A.

     (a) How many students earned an A?

     (b) What percent of the students earned an A?

6. Write fourteen billion in scientific notation.

7. Write 1.5×10^6 in standard form.

8. Use a unit multiplier to convert 600 mm to cm.

9. Write 350% as a mixed number.

10. Gabriella is 5 feet 2 inches tall. Lenora is 66 inches tall. Lenora is how many inches taller than Gabriella?

Refer to this figure to answer questions 11 and 12. Dimensions are in centimeters.

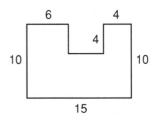

11. What is the area of the figure?

12. What is the perimeter of the figure?

Solve:

13. $6.54 + w = 10$

14. $\dfrac{9}{a} = \dfrac{45}{10}$

Add, subtract, multiply, or divide, as indicated:

15. $12^2 - 3^4 - 2^3 - \sqrt{144}$

16.
$$\begin{array}{r} 3 \text{ yd } 2 \text{ ft } 9 \text{ in.} \\ + \phantom{3 \text{ yd } 2 \text{ ft }} 1 \text{ ft } 8 \text{ in.} \\ \hline \end{array}$$

17. $2\dfrac{3}{4} + 2\dfrac{1}{6} + 3\dfrac{7}{8}$

18. $5\dfrac{1}{3} \cdot 5\dfrac{1}{4} \cdot 1\dfrac{3}{4}$

19. $0.8(0.25)(0.05)$

20. $4.5 \div 0.015$

Math 87 **by Hake & Saxon**

1. If a half gallon of milk costs $1.24, what is the cost per pint?

2. The cookie recipe called for oatmeal and raisins in the ratio of 3 to 1. If 4 cups of oatmeal were called for, how many cups of raisins were needed?

3. Marcie ran the 400-meter race 3 times. Her fastest time was 52.3 seconds. Her slowest time was 56.3 seconds. If her average time was 54.0 seconds, what was her time for the third race?

4. It is $2\frac{1}{2}$ miles to the end of the trail. If Paula runs to the end and back in 60 minutes, what is her average speed in miles per hour?

5. Fifty-four million, seven hundred thousand is how much greater than five million, eighty-nine thousand? Write the answer in words.

6. Draw a diagram of this statement. Then answer the questions that follow.

    Only four tenths of the print area of the newspaper carried news. The rest of the area was filled with advertisements.

    (a) What percent of the print area was filled with advertisements?

    (b) What was the ratio of news area to advertisement area?

7. Write 0.00205 in scientific notation.

8. Write 5.62×10^{-5} in standard form.

9. Use a unit multiplier to convert 1760 yards to feet.

10. Write $\frac{1}{25}$ as a percent.

Refer to this parallelogram to answer questions 11 and 12.

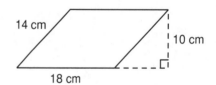

11. What is the perimeter of the parallelogram?

12. What is the area of the parallelogram?

Solve:

13. $\dfrac{4}{18} = \dfrac{n}{27}$

14. $p + 4.2 = 5$

Add, subtract, multiply, or divide, as indicated:

15. $10 + 10 \times 10 - 10 \div 10$

16. $10^4 - \sqrt{121} + 3^3$

17.
$$\begin{array}{r} 5 \text{ yd} \\ -\ 2 \text{ yd } 2 \text{ ft } 11 \text{ in.} \\ \hline \end{array}$$

18. $5\frac{7}{9} + \left(2\frac{1}{3} - 1\frac{1}{2}\right)$

19. $7\frac{1}{2} \div \left(2\frac{2}{5} \div 4\right)$

20. $4.3(0.05)(0.005)$

Math 87 by Hake & Saxon

1. If a half gallon of milk costs $1.28, what is the cost per pint?

2. The cookie recipe called for raisins and nuts in the ratio of 3 to 2. If 1 cup of nuts was called for, how many cups of raisins were needed?

3. Stacy ran the 200-meter race 3 times. Her fastest time was 26.3 seconds. Her slowest time was 30.3 seconds. If her average time was 28.0 seconds, what was her time for the third race?

4. It is $3\frac{1}{2}$ miles to the end of the trail. If Paul runs to the end of the trail and back in 60 minutes, what is his average speed in miles per hour?

5. Fourteen million, five hundred thousand is how much more than five million, forty-nine thousand? Write the answer in words.

6. Draw a diagram of this statement. Then answer the questions that follow.

   Only three tenths of the print area of the newspaper carried news. The rest of the area was filled with advertisements.

   (a) What percent of the print area was filled with advertisements?

   (b) What was the ratio of news area to advertisement area?

7. Write 0.00405 in scientific notation.

8. Write 6.25×10^{-5} in standard form.

9. Use a unit multiplier to convert 1320 yards to feet.

10. Write $\frac{1}{20}$ as a percent.

Refer to this parallelogram to answer questions 11 and 12. Dimensions are in inches.

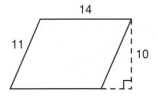

11. What is the perimeter of the parallelogram?

12. What is the area of the parallelogram?

Solve:

13. $\dfrac{10}{18} = \dfrac{n}{27}$

14. $p + 4.1 = 6$

Add, subtract, multiply, or divide, as indicated:

15. $5 + 5 \times 5 - 5 \div 5$

16. $10^3 - \sqrt{169} + 2^4$

17.
$$\begin{array}{r} 5 \text{ yd} \\ -\,3 \text{ yd } 1 \text{ ft } 7 \text{ in.} \\ \hline \end{array}$$

18. $5\frac{4}{9} + \left(3\frac{1}{2} - 1\frac{2}{3}\right)$

19. $3\frac{3}{4} \div \left(4 \div 2\frac{2}{5}\right)$

20. $2.2(0.05)(0.005)$

Math 87 by Hake & Saxon

Test 15 (Lesson 75), Form A   **SHOW YOUR WORK**   Name: _____

1. At 9:00 a.m. Marsha found a parking meter that still had 5 minutes until it expired. She quickly put a quarter, 1 dime, and a nickel into the meter and went to her meeting. If 5¢ buys 15 minutes of parking time, at what time will the meter expire?

Use the information in this paragraph to answer questions 2 and 3.

The Jenkins started their trip with a full tank of gas and 48,961 miles on their car. They stopped and filled the gas tank seven hours later with 14.0 gallons of gas. At that time the car's total mileage was 49,381.

2. What was the car's average speed in miles per hour for the first seven hours of the trip?

3. The Jenkins' car traveled an average of how many miles per gallon during the first seven hours of the trip?

4. The ratio of cetaceans to fish in the harbor was 3 to 13. How many fish were in the harbor if there were 390 cetaceans?

5. Draw a diagram of this statement. Then answer the questions that follow.

   Exit polls showed that 8 out of every 10 voters cast their ballot for the incumbent.

   (a) According to the exit polls, what percent of the voters cast their ballot for the incumbent?
   (b) According to the exit polls, what fraction of the voters did not cast their ballot for the incumbent?

6. What number is $\frac{3}{5}$ of 6?

7. Write two millionths in scientific notation.

8. Write 1.3×10^6 in standard form.

9. Use a unit multiplier to convert 9 yards to inches.

10. Sketch a number line to show this addition problem: $(-3) + (+5)$

11. Complete the table.

Fraction	Decimal	Percent
(a)	0.6	(b)
(c)	(d)	120%

12. Evaluate: $ab - a + bc$ if $a = 4$, $b = 2$, and $c = 3$

Refer to this figure to answer questions 13 and 14. Dimensions are in inches.

13. What is the perimeter?

14. What is the area?

Solve:

15. $\frac{15}{25} = \frac{9}{m}$

16. $p - \frac{1}{2} = \frac{1}{3}$

Add, subtract, multiply, or divide, as indicated:

17. $10 - (8 - 3) - 3 \div 3 + 1$

18.
```
  2 gal 2 qt 2 pt
- 1 gal 3 qt 1 pt 2 oz
```

19. $4\frac{1}{3} - \left(2\frac{1}{3} \cdot 1\frac{1}{2}\right)$

20. $0.01 \div (0.01 \div 0.001)$

Math 87 **by Hake & Saxon**

1. At 9 a.m. Marco found a parking meter that still had 10 minutes until it expired. He quickly put in a quarter, a dime, and 2 nickels. If 5¢ buys 10 minutes of parking time, at what time will the meter expire?

Use the information in this paragraph to answer questions 2 and 3.

   The Jansens started their trip with a full tank of gas and 36,830 miles on their car. They stopped and filled their gas tank five hours later with 10 gallons of gas. At that time the car's total mileage was 37,080.

2. The Jansens had traveled at an average speed of how many miles per hour?

3. The Jansens' car had averaged how many miles per gallon?

4. The ratio of mammals to reptiles on the desert acreage was 4 to 5. If there were 360 mammals on the desert acreage, how many reptiles were there?

5. Draw a diagram of this statement. Then answer the questions that follow.

   Exit polls showed that 6 out of every 10 voters cast their ballot for the incumbent.

   (a) According to the exit polls, what percent of the voters cast their ballot for the incumbent?

   (b) According to the exit polls, what fraction of the voters did not cast their ballot for the incumbent?

6. What number is $\frac{3}{5}$ of 8?

7. Write three millionths in scientific notation.

8. Write 1.5×10^5 in standard form.

9. Use a unit multiplier to convert 12 yards to inches.

10. Sketch a number line to show this addition problem: $(-2) + (+5)$

11. Complete the table.

Fraction	Decimal	Percent
(a)	0.8	(b)
(c)	(d)	140%

12. Evaluate: $ab - a + bc$ if $a = 2$, $b = 3$, and $c = 4$

Refer to this figure to answer questions 13 and 14.
Dimensions are in centimeters.

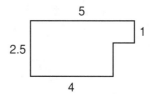

13. What is the perimeter?

14. What is the area?

Solve:

15. $\dfrac{15}{25} = \dfrac{12}{m}$

16. $p - \dfrac{1}{3} = \dfrac{1}{4}$

Add, subtract, multiply, or divide, as indicated:

17. $10 + (8 - 3) - 3 \div 3 + 1$

18.
```
  2 gal 1 qt 1 pt
- 1 gal 2 qt 1 pt 5 oz
```

19. $4\dfrac{2}{3} - \left(2\dfrac{1}{4} \cdot 1\dfrac{1}{3}\right)$

20. $0.1 \div (0.01 \div 0.1)$

Math 87 **by Hake & Saxon**

1. Six hundred ninety-four ten-thousandths is how much more than fifty-seven thousandths? Write the answer in words.

2. Justin worked for 7 hours and earned $38.50. How much did he earn per hour?

3. Three sevenths of the possible outcomes were favorable, while the rest of the possible outcomes were unfavorable.

    (a) What fraction of the possible outcomes were unfavorable?

    (b) What was the ratio of favorable to unfavorable outcomes?

4. What is the average of $4\frac{1}{2}$, $3\frac{1}{3}$, 2, and $2\frac{1}{6}$?

5. What number is 25% of 96?

6. Draw a diagram of this statement. Then answer the questions that follow.

    Joel gave $\frac{1}{4}$ of his 236 postage stamps to his sister.

    (a) What percent of his postage stamps did Joel give to his sister?

    (b) How many postage stamps did Joel have left?

7. Write eight hundred-thousandths in scientific notation.

8. Write 2.4×10^{-4} in standard form.

9. Replace the circle with the proper comparison symbol.

    4.5 km $\bigcirc$ 4500 m

10. Divide 7 by 0.27 and write the answer rounded to the nearest whole number.

11. Find this sum: $(+6) + (-11) + (+5) + (-7)$

12. Complete the table.

Fraction	Decimal	Percent
$\frac{1}{8}$	(a)	(b)
(c)	0.12	(d)

13. Find the area of this triangle. Dimensions are in centimeters.

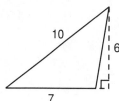

14. Evaluate: $ab + a + b$ if $a = \frac{1}{4}$ and $b = \frac{1}{5}$

Solve:

15. $\dfrac{w}{45} = \dfrac{8}{20}$

16. $2.5c = 0.125$

Add, subtract, multiply, or divide, as indicated:

17. $2 \text{ m} - 25 \text{ cm} = \underline{\quad} \text{ cm}$

18. $4\frac{1}{4} + \left(2\frac{1}{6} - 1\frac{1}{3}\right)$

19. $5\frac{1}{4}\left(4 \div 1\frac{1}{2}\right)$

20. $0.5(0.1)(1.2)$

Math 87 by Hake & Saxon

1. Five hundred sixty ten-thousandths is how much more than forty-five thousandths? Write the answer in words.

2. Julie worked for 6 hours and earned $39.00. How much did she earn per hour?

3. Three fifths of the possible outcomes were favorable, while the rest of the possible outcomes were unfavorable.

   (a) What fracton of the possible outcomes were unfavorable?
   (b) What was the ratio of favorable to unfavorable outcomes?

4. What is the average of $5\frac{1}{2}$, 3, $4\frac{1}{3}$, and $3\frac{1}{6}$?

5. What number is 6% of 850?

6. Draw a diagram of this statement. Then answer the questions that follow.
   David gave $\frac{1}{5}$ of his 235 baseball cards to his sister.

   (a) What percent of his baseball cards did David give to his sister?
   (b) How many baseball cards did David have left?

7. Write six ten-thousandths in scientific notation.

8. Write 7.5×10^{-3} in standard form.

9. Replace the circle with the proper comparison symbol.
   $$1.5 \text{ kg} \bigcirc 150\text{g}$$

10. Divide 8 by 0.15 and write the answer rounded to the nearest whole number.

11. Find this sum: $(-3) + (+3) + (-8) + (+12)$

12. Complete the table.

Fraction	Decimal	Percent
$\frac{3}{8}$	(a)	(b)
(c)	0.15	(d)

13. Find the area of this triangle. Dimensions are in centimeters.

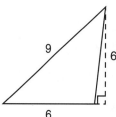

14. Evaluate: $ab + a + b$ if $a = \frac{1}{3}$ and $b = \frac{1}{5}$

Solve:

15. $\dfrac{w}{45} = \dfrac{12}{20}$

16. $1.5m = 2.25$

Add, subtract, multiply, or divide, as indicated:

17. $2 \text{ m} - 15 \text{ cm} = $ _____ cm

18. $3\frac{3}{4} \div \left(2\frac{1}{6} - 1\frac{1}{3}\right)$

19. $3\frac{3}{4} + 5\frac{1}{6} + 2\frac{1}{2}$

20. $0.05(0.1)(2.4)$

Math 87 by Hake & Saxon

1. Maria ran 4 laps of the track at the same pace. If it took $4\frac{1}{2}$ minutes to run the first 3 laps, how long did it take her to run all 4 laps?

2. The average of three numbers is 3. If the greatest is 4.6 and the least is 1.4, what is the third number?

3. The ratio of left-handed to right-handed students in the school was 3 to 14. If the total number in both categories was 714, how many right-handed students were in the school?

4. How far will a migrating duck fly in 7 hours at an average speed of 21 miles per hour?

5. Draw a diagram of this statement. Then answer the questions that follow.

    Tom has read $\frac{3}{8}$ of the 480 pages in the book.

    (a) How many pages are left to read?

    (b) What is the ratio of pages read to pages not yet read?

6. Find the circumference of each circle.

    (a)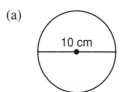

    10 cm

    Use 3.14 for π

    (b)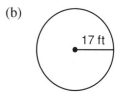

    17 ft

    Leave π as π

Refer to the figure to answer questions 7 and 8. Dimensions are in millimeters.

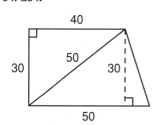

7. What is the area of the right triangle?

8. What is the area of the isosceles triangle?

9. Write 3,600,000,000 in scientific notation.

10. What is 25% of 1600?

11. What number is $\frac{5}{8}$ of 24?

12. Complete the table.

13. Find this sum.

    $(-5) + (-5) + (+7) + (-2)$

Fraction	Decimal	Percent
$\frac{1}{3}$	(a)	(b)
(c)	0.32	(d)

14. Use a unit multiplier to convert 10 tons to pounds.

15. Evaluate: $\dfrac{x + y}{xy}$ if $x = \dfrac{1}{8}$ and $y = \dfrac{1}{3}$

Solve:

16. $\dfrac{3}{4} + n = 2\dfrac{1}{8}$

17. $\dfrac{y}{16} = \dfrac{1.2}{0.6}$

Add, subtract, multiply, or divide, as indicated:

18. $1\text{ kg} - 705\text{ g} = \underline{\quad} \text{ g}$

19. $5^2 - \sqrt{10^2 - 8^2}$

20. $3\dfrac{3}{4} \div \left(5\dfrac{1}{2} - 2\dfrac{1}{5}\right)$

Math 87 by Hake & Saxon

1. Marcus ran 4 laps of the track at the same pace. If it took 3 minutes 45 seconds to run the first 3 laps, how long did it take Marcus to run all four laps?

2. The average of three numbers is 3. If the greatest is 5.6 and the least is 1.4, what is the third number?

3. The ratio of left-handed to right-handed students in the school was 2 to 13. If the total number in both categories was 390, how many right-handed students were in the school?

4. How far will a migrating duck fly in 7 hours at an average speed of 28 miles per hour?

5. Draw a diagram of this statement. Then answer the questions that follow.

    Tom has read $\frac{5}{8}$ of the 360 pages in the book.

    (a) How many pages are left to read?

    (b) What is the ratio of pages read to pages not yet read?

6. Find the circumference of each circle.

    (a)
    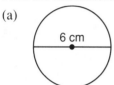
    6 cm

    Use 3.14 for π

    (b)

    7 in.

    Use $\frac{22}{7}$ for π

Refer to the figure to answer questions 7 and 8. Dimensions are in millimeters.

7. What is the area of the right triangle?

8. What is the area of the isosceles triangle?

9. Write 3,650,000,000 in scientific notation.

10. What is 25% of 1200?

11. What number is $\frac{3}{5}$ of 35?

12. Complete the table.

13. Find this sum.

    $(-5) + (-7) + (+5) + (-2)$

FRACTION	DECIMAL	PERCENT
$\frac{2}{3}$	(a)	(b)
(c)	0.36	(d)

14. Use a unit multiplier to convert 16 tons to pounds.

15. Evaluate: $\dfrac{x + y}{xy}$ if $x = \dfrac{1}{4}$ and $y = \dfrac{1}{5}$

Solve:

16. $\dfrac{7}{8} + n = 2\dfrac{1}{4}$

17. $\dfrac{w}{16} = \dfrac{0.6}{1.2}$

Add, subtract, multiply, or divide, as indicated:

18. $1 \text{ kg} - 507 \text{ g} = \underline{\quad} \text{ g}$

19. $3^2 - \sqrt{5^2 - 4^2}$

20. $7\dfrac{1}{2} \div \left(5\dfrac{1}{2} \div 2\dfrac{1}{5}\right)$

Math 87 by Hake & Saxon

1. It was 96 kilometers from Perry to Medford. David raced to Medford and idled back. If the round trip took 8 hours, what was his average speed in kilometers per hour?

2. The ratio of dogs to cats in the neighborhood was 3 to 7. If there were 42 dogs in the neighborhood, how many cats were there?

3. Using a tape measure, Becky Jo found that the circumference of the great redwood was 900 cm. She estimated that its diameter was 300 cm. Was her estimate a little too large or a little too small? Why?

4. Pistachios were priced at 3 pounds for $6.99.
   (a) What was the price per pound?
   (b) How much would 10 pounds of pistachios cost?

5. If the product of six tenths and three tenths is subtracted from the sum of two tenths and four tenths, what is the difference?

6. Draw a diagram of this statement. Then answer the questions that follow.

   Three fifths of the baker's 60 cookies were chocolate cookies.

   (a) How many of the baker's cookies were chocolate?
   (b) What percent of the baker's cookies were not chocolate cookies?

7. Replace the circle with the proper comparison symbol.
$$3 - 5 \bigcirc 3 + (-5)$$

8. Find the circumference of each of these circles.

   (a)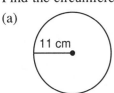

   11 cm

   Leave π as π

   (b)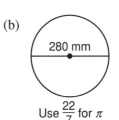

   280 mm

   Use $\frac{22}{7}$ for π

9. Write each of these numbers in scientific notation.
   (a) 11×10^{-7} (b) 11×10^7

10. What is the sum of the three numbers marked by arrows on this number line?

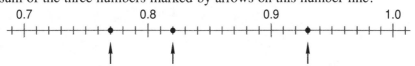

11. What number is 15% of 1400?

12. What number is $\frac{1}{8}$ of 100?

13. Complete the table.

14. Simplify: $(-6) + (-3) - (-1) - (+4)$

15. Use a unit multiplier to convert 8000 g to kg.

16. Evaluate: $ab - (a - b)$ if $a = 0.5$ and $b = 0.4$

Fraction	Decimal	Percent
$\frac{1}{12}$	(a)	(b)
(c)	(d)	18%

Solve:

17. $q + 36 = 42.6$

18. $5n = 32$

Add, subtract, multiply, or divide, as indicated:

19. $8.6 \times 5\frac{1}{4}$ (decimal)

20. $1\frac{1}{3} \div \left(3\frac{1}{2} \cdot 2 \right)$

Math 87 by Hake & Saxon

1. It was 32 miles from Moonridge to Mentone. Malcomb coasted most of the way to Mentone and then pedalled back hard. If the round trip took 4 hours, what was his average speed in miles per hour?

2. The ratio of dogs to cats in the neighborhood was 2 to 3. If there were 30 dogs in the neighborhood, how many cats were there?

3. Using a tape measure, Justin found that the circumference of the great redwood was 600 cm. He estimated that its diameter was 200 cm. Was his estimate a little too large or a little too small? Why?

4. Parsnips were priced at 3 pounds for $1.23.
   (a) What was the price per pound?
   (b) How much would 10 pounds of parsnips cost?

5. If the product of four tenths and six tenths is subtracted from the sum of four tenths and six tenths, what is the difference?

6. Draw a diagram of this statement. Then answer the questions that follow.

   Two fifths of the baker's 60 cookies were oatmeal.

   (a) How many of the baker's cookies were oatmeal?
   (b) What percent of the baker's cookies were not oatmeal?

7. Replace the circle with the proper comparison symbol.
   $$4 - 6 \bigcirc 4 + (-6)$$

8. Find the circumference of each circle.

   (a)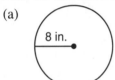

   (b)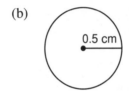

   Leave π as π Use 3.14 for π

9. Write each of these numbers in scientific notation.
   (a) 12×10^{-6} (b) 12×10^{6}

10. What is the sum of the three numbers marked by arrows on this number line?

    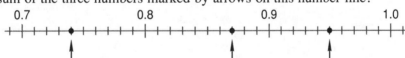

11. What number is 15% of 1200?

12. What number is $\frac{1}{8}$ of 200?

13. Complete the table.

14. Simplify: $(-6) + (+3) - (-2) - (+5)$

15. Use a unit multiplier to convert 9000 g to kg.

16. Evaluate: $ab - (a - b)$ if $a = 0.6$ and $b = 0.4$

Fraction	Decimal	Percent
$\frac{1}{6}$	(a)	(b)
(c)	(d)	14%

Solve:

17. $q + 26 = 42.6$ 18. $6n = 33$

Add, subtract, multiply, or divide, as indicated:

19. $4.6 \times 3\frac{1}{4}$ (decimal)   20. $2\frac{2}{3} \div \left(3\frac{1}{3} \cdot 2\right)$

Math 87 by Hake & Saxon

1. Write a proportion to solve this problem. In the land of Feather, 6 lifts equal 5 zooms. How many lifts are equal to 35 zooms?

2. What is the average of the 2 numbers marked by arrows on this number line?

Refer to this figure to answer questions 3 and 4.
Dimensions are in centimeters.

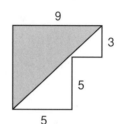

3. What is the perimeter of the hexagon?

4. What is the area of the shaded region?

5. Four squared is how much greater than the square root of 4?

6. Use a ratio box to solve this problem. Five hundred fifty students attended the assembly. If the ratio of boys to girls in the assembly was 6 to 5, how many girls attended the assembly?

7. Use a unit multiplier to convert 6.4 g to milligrams.

8. Draw a diagram of this statement. Then answer the questions that follow.

    In the first fifth of the season the Madrigals played 12 games.

    (a) How many games did the Madrigals play during the whole season?

    (b) If the Madrigals won $\frac{2}{3}$ of their games during the whole season, how many games did they win?

Write an equation to solve Problems 9 and 10.

9. Seventy-two is four fifths of what number?

10. One-tenth of what number is 201?

11. Simplify:

    (a) $-9(-2)$ (b) $-9(+6)$ (c) $\dfrac{-9}{-3}$ (d) $\dfrac{9}{-1}$

12. If each edge of a cube is 5 cm, what is the volume of the cube?

13. Find the circumference of each of these circles.

    (a)   (b)

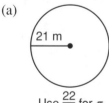

Use $\frac{22}{7}$ for π

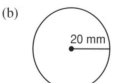

Leave π as π

14. Complete the table.

15. Evaluate: $10m - (my - y^2)$ if $m = 10$ and $y = 6$

Solve and check. Show your work.

Fraction	Decimal	Percent
$\frac{1}{5}$	(a)	(b)
(c)	0.45	(d)

16. $\dfrac{2}{3}y = 8$ 17. $m + 1.6 = 3$

Add, subtract, multiply, or divide, as indicated:

18. $\dfrac{\$600}{1\ wk} \cdot \dfrac{1\ wk}{5\ days} \cdot \dfrac{1\ day}{8\ hr}$ 19. $(-7) - (-4) + (-3)$ 20. $3\dfrac{3}{4} \div \left(1\dfrac{2}{3} + 2\dfrac{1}{2}\right)$

Math 87 **by Hake & Saxon**

1. Write a proportion to solve this problem. In the land of Fealty, 4 vows equal 6 oaths. How many vows are equal to 72 oaths?

2. What is the average of the 2 numbers marked by arrows on this number line?

Refer to this figure to answer questions 3 and 4. Dimensions are in centimeters.

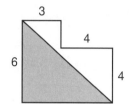

3. What is the perimeter of the hexagon?

4. What is the area of the shaded region?

5. Nine squared is how much greater than the square root of 9?

6. Use a ratio box to solve this problem. Five hundred fifty students attended the assembly. If the ratio of boys to girls in the assembly was 7 to 4, how many girls attended the assembly?

7. Use a unit multiplier to convert 4.6 g to milligrams.

8. Draw a diagram of this statement. Then answer the questions that follow.

   In the first quarter of the season the Matadors played 12 games.

   (a) How many games did the Matadors play during the whole season?

   (b) If the Matadors won $\frac{2}{3}$ of their games during the whole season, how many games did they win?

Write an equation to solve Problems 9 and 10.

9. Seventy-two is three fourths of what number?

10. One-tenth of what number is 120?

11. Simplify:

    (a) $-8(-3)$ (b) $-6(+3)$ (c) $\dfrac{-8}{-2}$ (d) $\dfrac{9}{-3}$

12. If each edge of a cube is 3 cm, what is the volume of the cube?

13. Find the circumference of each of these circles.

    (a)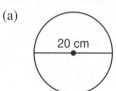

    (b)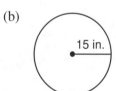

    Use 3.14 for π Leave π as π

14. Complete the table.

15. Evaluate: $10m - (my - y^2)$ if $m = 6$ and $y = 3$

Fraction	Decimal	Percent
$\frac{3}{5}$	(a)	(b)
(c)	0.35	(d)

Solve and check. Show your work.

16. $\dfrac{3}{4}y = 12$ 17. $x + 2.6 = 5$

Add, subtract, multiply, or divide, as indicated:

18. $\dfrac{\$500}{1 \text{ wk}} \cdot \dfrac{1 \text{ wk}}{5 \text{ days}} \cdot \dfrac{1 \text{ day}}{8 \text{ hr}}$ 19. $(-6) - (-5) + (-4)$ 20. $1\dfrac{7}{8} \div \left(4\dfrac{1}{6} - 2\dfrac{1}{2}\right)$

1. Tim mowed lawns for 2 hours and earned $4.50 per hour. Then he washed windows for 4 hours and earned $3.45 per hour. What was Tim's average earnings per hour for all 6 hours?

2. Evaluate: $x + (x^2 - xy) - y$ if $x = 5$ and $y = 4$

3. Replace the circle with the proper comparison symbol.

$$a \bigcirc b \text{ if } a - b = 1$$

Use a ratio box to solve Problems 4 and 5.

4. When Nelson cleaned his room he found that the ratio of clean clothes to dirty clothes was 3 to 4. If 35 articles of clothing were discovered, how many were clean?

5. In 25 minutes, 400 customers entered the attraction. At this rate, how many customers would enter the attraction in 1 hour?

6. The diameter of a round skating rink is 15 m. Find the circumference of the rink to the nearest meter.

7. Use a unit multiplier to convert $3\frac{1}{2}$ qts to pints.

8. Graph this inequality on a number line: $x > -5$

9. Nathan found that the 14 inches from his knee joint to his hip joint was $\frac{1}{4}$ of his total height. What was Nathan's total height in inches?

10. Simplify:

    (a) $\dfrac{400}{-5}$ (b) $\dfrac{-720}{-12}$ (c) $15(-20)$ (d) $+12(80)$

11. Complete the table.

Write an equation to solve Problems 12 and 13.

12. Six hundred is $\dfrac{4}{9}$ of what number?

13. What number is 35% of 40?

FRACTION	DECIMAL	PERCENT
$\frac{5}{6}$	(a)	(b)
(c)	0.6	(d)

14. Simplify: $\dfrac{5\frac{1}{3}}{100}$

15. Find the area of this trapezoid. Dimensions are in meters.

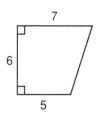

Solve and check. Show all steps.

16. $\dfrac{3}{5}m = 48$ 17. $1.5 = x - 0.08$

Add, subtract, multiply, or divide, as indicated:

18. $\dfrac{3^3 + 2 \cdot 5 - 3 \cdot 2^2}{\sqrt{25}}$ 19. $4\frac{2}{3} \div 1.4$ (fraction)   20. $-26 - (-42) + (+35)$

Math 87 by Hake & Saxon

1. Tim mowed lawns for 2 hours and earned $4.50 per hour. Then he washed windows for 3 hours and earned $3.45 per hour. What was Tim's average earnings per hour for all 5 hours?

2. Evaluate: $x + (x^2 - xy) - y$ if $x = 5$ and $y = 3$

3. Replace the circle with the proper comparison symbol.
    $$a \bigcirc b \text{ if } a \div b = 1$$

Use a ratio box to solve Problems 4 and 5.

4. When Meredith cleaned her room she found that the ratio of clean clothes to dirty clothes was 2 to 5. If 35 articles of clothing were discovered, how many were clean?

5. In 25 minutes, 300 customers entered the attraction. At this rate, how many customers would enter the attraction in one hour?

6. The diameter of a round skating rink is 14 m. Find the circumference of the rink to the nearest meter.

7. Use a unit multiplier to convert $2\frac{1}{2}$ qts to pints.

8. Graph this inequality on a number line: $x \geq -5$

9. Jason found that the 16 inches from his knee joint to his hip joint was $\frac{1}{4}$ of his total height. What was his total height in inches?

10. Simplify:

    (a) $\dfrac{300}{-5}$ (b) $\dfrac{-840}{-12}$ (c) $15(-30)$ (d) $12(+60)$

11. Complete the table.

Fraction	Decimal	Percent
$\frac{1}{9}$	(a)	(b)
(c)	0.8	(d)

Write an equation to solve Problems 12 and 13.

12. Six hundred is $\dfrac{5}{9}$ of what number?

13. What number is 35% of 60?

14. Simplify: $\dfrac{6\frac{2}{3}}{100}$

15. Find the area of this trapezoid. Dimensions are in meters.

Solve and check. Show all steps.

16. $\dfrac{3}{5}m = 45$ 17. $2.5 = x - 0.07$

Add, subtract, multiply, or divide, as indicated:

18. $\dfrac{2^3 + 3 \cdot 5 - 2 \cdot 3^2}{\sqrt{3^2 + 4^2}}$ 19. $1.4 \div 4\frac{2}{3}$ (fraction)   20. $-23 - (-36) + (-15)$

Math 87 by Hake & Saxon

Test 21 (Lesson 105), Form A   SHOW YOUR WORK   Name: _____

1. The team's ratio of games won to games played was 5 to 6. If the team played 36 games, how many games did the team fail to win?

2. Find the (a) mean, (b) median, (c) mode, and (d) range for the following scores:

   60, 70, 90, 70, 80, 65, 95, 80, 100, 60

3. Elmo was chagrined to find that the ratio of dandelions to peonies in the garden was 11 to 4. If there were 36 peonies in the garden, then how many dandelions were there?

4. Use a unit multiplier to convert 0.47 liters to milliliters.

5. Graph $x \le -3$ on a number line.

Use a ratio box to solve Problems 6 and 7.

6. If sound travels 2 miles in 10 seconds, how far does sound travel in 2 minutes?

7. Before the clowns arrived, only 35% of the children wore happy faces. If 117 children did not wear happy faces, how many children were there in all?

8. Draw a diagram of this statement. Then answer the questions that follow.

   Forty-five thousand dollars was raised in the charity drive. This was nine tenths of the goal.

   (a) The goal of the charity drive was to raise how much money?

   (b) The drive fell short of the goal by what percent?

9. Compare: $2a \bigcirc a^2$ if a is a whole number

10. A certain rectangular prism is 4 inches long, 2 inches wide, and 3 inches high. Sketch the figure and find its volume.

11. Find the area of this circle. Dimensions are in inches.

6

Use 3.14 for π

12. Complete the table.

Fraction	Decimal	Percent
$\frac{3}{40}$	(a)	(b)
(c)	(d)	$3\frac{1}{3}\%$

13. Name this shape and find its perimeter.

14 cm, 10.5 cm, 10 cm, 10.5 cm, 14 cm

14. Find the area of the shape in Problem 13.

15. Multiply $(2.5 \times 10^6)(1.3 \times 10^9)$ and write the product in scientific notation.

Solve and check. Show all steps.

16. $15.4 = 1.4p$

17. $z + \frac{4}{9} = 1\frac{1}{5}$

Add, subtract, multiply, or divide, as indicated:

18. $3\{25 - [7^2 - 4(11 - 4)]\}$

19. $0.7 \div \left(7\frac{1}{2} - 2\frac{5}{6}\right)$

20. $(-3) + (-4) - (-7) + (-8)$

Math 87 by Hake & Saxon

1. The team's ratio of games won to games played was 4 to 7. If the team played 35 games, how many games did the team fail to win?

2. Find the (a) mean, (b) median, (c) mode, and (d) range for the following scores:

   50, 60, 80, 60, 70, 55, 85, 70, 90, 50

3. Milo was chagrined to find that the ratio of dandelions to daisies in the garden was 9 to 4. If there were 36 daisies in the garden, how many dandelions were there?

4. Use a unit multiplier to convert 0.84 liters to milliliters.

5. Graph $x \geq -3$ on a number line.

Use a ratio box to solve Problems 6 and 7.

6. If sound travels 2 miles in 10 seconds, how long does sound take to travel 5 miles?

7. Before the clowns arrived only 45% of the children wore happy faces. If 110 children did not wear happy faces, how many children were there in all?

8. Draw a diagram of this statement. Then answer the questions that follow.

   Forty-two thousand dollars was raised in the charity drive. This was seven tenths of the goal.

   (a) The goal of the charity drive was to raise how much money?

   (b) The drive fell short of the goal by what percent?

9. Compare: $2a \bigcirc a^2$ if $a > 2$

10. A certain rectangular prism is 5 inches long, 2 inches wide, and 3 inches high. Sketch the figure and find its volume.

11. Find the area of this circle. Dimensions are in inches.

Use $\frac{22}{7}$ for π

12. Complete the table.

Fraction	Decimal	Percent
$\frac{3}{20}$	(a)	(b)
(c)	(d)	$1\frac{2}{3}\%$

13. Name this shape and find its perimeter.

28 mm
21 mm
20 mm 21 mm
28 mm

14. Find the area of the shape in Problem 13.

15. Multiply $(2.4 \times 10^6)(1.5 \times 10^7)$ and write the product in scientific notation.

Solve and check. Show all steps.

16. $16.8 = 1.4p$

17. $y + \dfrac{5}{9} = 1\dfrac{4}{5}$

Add, subtract, multiply, or divide, as indicated:

18. $2\{25 - [7^2 - 4(11 - 5)]\}$

19. $0.8 \div \left(5\dfrac{1}{2} - 2\dfrac{5}{6}\right)$ (fraction)

20. $(-4) + (-5) - (-8) + (-7)$

Math 87 by Hake & Saxon

1. In the forest there were lions and tigers and bears. The ratio of lions to tigers was 3 to 2. The ratio of tigers to bears was 3 to 4. If there were 9 lions, how many bears were there? (*Hint*: First find how many tigers there were.)

2. Bill measured the shoe box and found that it was 25 cm long, 15 cm wide, and 8 cm high. What was the volume of the shoe box?

3. A baseball player's batting average is found by dividing the number of hits by the number of at-bats and rounding the result to the nearest thousandth. If Erika had 24 hits in 57 at-bats, what was her batting average?

4. Use two unit multipliers to convert 81 square feet to square yards.

5. Graph the negative integers greater than -3.

6. Draw a diagram of this statement. Then answer the questions that follow.

    Jimmy bought the shirt for $36. This was $\frac{3}{4}$ of the regular price.

    (a) What was the regular price of the shirt?

    (b) Jimmy bought the shirt for what percent of the regular price?

Use the information in this figure to answer questions 7 and 8.

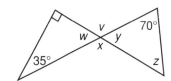

7. What is $m\angle w$?

8. What is $m\angle z$?

9. What is the circumference of this circle?

14 in.

Use $\frac{22}{7}$ for π

10. Find the area of this trapezoid.

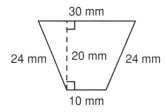

30 mm

24 mm   20 mm   24 mm

10 mm

11. Compare: $a^2 \bigcirc a$ if $a = 0.9$

12. Complete the table.

FRACTION	DECIMAL	PERCENT
(a)	0.06	(b)

13. Use a ratio box to solve this problem. Forty-five percent of the 5000 fast food customers ordered a hamburger. How many of the customers did not order a hamburger?

14. Forty is what percent of 200?

15. How many degrees is $\frac{1}{6}$ of a full circle?

16. Multiply $(1.25 \times 10^{-3})(8 \times 10^{-5})$ and write the product in scientific notation.

Solve and check. Show all steps.

17. $\frac{4}{9}p = 112$

18. $12.3 = 5.73 + f$

Add, subtract, multiply, or divide, as indicated:

19. $4.2 \times \frac{1}{20} \times 10^2$ (decimal)

20. $(-5) - (+6)(-2) - (-3)(-4)$

Math 87 by Hake & Saxon

1. In the forest there were lions and tigers and bears. The ratio of lions to tigers was 2 to 3. The ratio of tigers to bears was 4 to 3. If there were 16 lions, how many bears were there? (*Hint*: First find how many tigers there were.)

2. The shoe box was 30 cm long, 15 cm wide, and 10 cm high. What was the volume of the shoe box?

3. A baseball player's batting average is found by dividing the number of hits by the number of at-bats and rounding the result to the nearest thousandth. If Eric had 21 hits in 51 at-bats, what was his batting average?

4. Use two unit multipliers to convert 54 square feet to square yards.

5. Graph the negative integers greater than -4.

6. Draw a diagram of this statement. Then answer the questions that follow.

   Jimmy bought the shirt for $32. This was $\frac{4}{5}$ of the regular price.

   (a) What was the regular price of the shirt?

   (b) Jimmy bought the shirt for what percent of the regular price?

Use the information in this figure to answer questions 7 and 8.

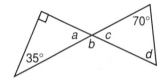

7. What is $m\angle a$?

8. What is $m\angle d$?

9. What is the circumference of this circle?

15 in.

Use 3.14 for π

10. Find the area of this trapezoid.

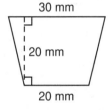

30 mm

20 mm

20 mm

11. Compare: $a^2 \bigcirc a$ if $a = 0.5$

12. Complete the table.

FRACTION	DECIMAL	PERCENT
(a)	0.08	(b)

13. Use a ratio box to solve this problem. Forty-five percent of the 3000 fast food customers ordered a hamburger. How many of the customers did not order a hamburger?

14. Eighty is what percent of 200?

15. How many degrees is $\frac{1}{8}$ of a full circle?

16. Multiply $(2.5 \times 10^{-3})(4 \times 10^{-6})$ and write the product in scientific notation.

Solve and check. Show all steps.

17. $\frac{4}{9}m = 144$

18. $12.5 = 1.25 + f$

Add, subtract, multiply, or divide, as indicated:

19. $8.4 \times \frac{1}{20} \times 10^3$ (decimal)

20. $(-3) - (+4)(-2) - (-2)(-6)$

1. After 3 tests Amanda's average score was 88. What score must she earn on her next test to have a 4-test average of 90?

2. Forty-five of the 80 students in the club were girls. What was the ratio of boys to girls in the club?

3. Three dozen juice bars cost $4.80. At that rate, what would be the cost of 60 juice bars?

4. The county's population increased 20% from 1980 to 1990. If the population in 1980 was 250,000, what was the population in 1990?

5. Due to the unexpected cold weather, the cost of tomatoes increased 50 percent in one month. If the cost after the increase was 60¢ per pound, what was the cost before the increase?

6. Write an equation to solve this problem. Sixty is what percent of 80?

7. Use two unit multipliers to convert 1000 cm² to mm².

8. If $x = -3$ and $y = 4x - 1$, then y equals what number?

9. Find the area of this trapezoid. Dimensions are in millimeters.

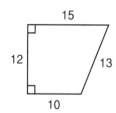

10. The price of the stereo was $96.00. The tax rate was 6%.

    (a) What was the tax on the stereo?

    (b) What was the total price of the stereo including tax?

11. Multiply $(7 \times 10^{-4})(4 \times 10^8)$ and write the result in scientific notation.

12. Complete the table.

Fraction	Decimal	Percent
$3\frac{1}{3}$	(a)	(b)
(c)	(d)	2%

13. Graph the whole numbers less than 3.

Solve and check. Show all steps.

14. $1\frac{2}{3}x = 60$

15. $m - 0.45 = 5.4$

Add, subtract, multiply, or divide, as indicated:

16. $(2 \cdot 5)^2 - 2(5)^2$

17. $1 \text{ L} - 200 \text{ mL}$

18. $4 - \left(2\frac{2}{3} - 1.5\right)$ (fraction)

19. $\dfrac{(-6)(-10)(-8)}{(-3)(-5)(-4)}$

20. $6 - 9 + 4 - 15 + 3(-4)$

Math 87 by Hake & Saxon

1. After 4 tests Andrew's average score was 88. What score must he earn on the next test to have a 5-test average of 90?

2. Fifty of the 80 students in the club were girls. What was the ratio of boys to girls in the club?

3. Two dozen juice bars cost $4.80. At that rate what would be the cost of 60 juice bars?

4. The county's population increased 20% from 1980 to 1990. If the population in 1980 was 300,000, what was the population in 1990?

5. Due to the unexpected cold weather, the cost of tomatoes increased 50 percent in one month. If the cost after the increase was 90¢ per pound, what was the cost before the increase?

6. Write an equation to solve this problem. Sixty-four is what percent of 80?

7. Use two unit multipliers to convert 10 cm^2 to mm^2.

8. If $x = -4$ and $y = 2x - 1$, then y equals what number?

9. Find the area of this trapezoid. Dimensions are in centimeters.

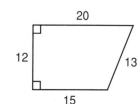

10. The price of the stereo was $124.00. The tax rate was 6%.

    (a) What was the tax on the stereo?

    (b) What was the total price of the stereo including tax?

11. Multiply $(8 \times 10^{-3})(2 \times 10^{10})$ and write the result in scientific notation.

12. Complete the table.

Fraction	Decimal	Percent
$1\frac{1}{3}$	(a)	(b)
(c)	(d)	4%

13. Graph the whole numbers greater than -3.

Solve and check. Show all steps.

14. $3\frac{1}{3}x = 60$

15. $w - 0.35 = 4.2$

Add, subtract, multiply, or divide, as indicated:

16. $(3 \cdot 4)^2 - 3(4)^2$

17. $1\,\text{g} - 100\,\text{mg}$

18. $6 - \left(2\frac{1}{3} - 1.5\right)$ (fraction)

19. $\dfrac{(-6)(-10)(-8)}{(-15)(-4)}$

20. $7 - 10 + 6 - 12 + 4(-3)$

Math 87 by Hake & Saxon

1. Jorge's average score on the first 3 tests was 88. His average score on the next 5 tests was 84. What was his average score on all 8 tests?

2. Use a ratio box to solve this problem. After working 6 months, Gina received a raise of 25%. If her previous pay was $7.20 per hour, what was her hourly pay after the raise?

3. Write an equation to solve this problem. Seventy is what percent of 50?

4. Use two unit multipliers to convert 1.6 m² to cm².

5. Draw a diagram of this statement. Then answer the questions that follow.

    Five eggs were cracked. This was $\frac{1}{6}$ of the total number of eggs in the flat.

    (a) How many eggs were in the flat?
    (b) What percent of the eggs in the flat were not cracked?

6. Evaluate: $\dfrac{a + b}{c}$ if $a = -6$, $b = -4$, and $c = -2$

7. The perimeter of a certain square is 12 inches. Find the area of the square in square inches.

8. What is the probability of this spinner

    (a) stopping on a vowel?
    (b) stopping on a consonent?

9. Find the volume of this triangular prism. Dimensions are in centimeters.

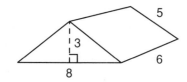

10. Find the area of this circle.

    Use 3.14 for π

11. Find the total price, including 6% tax, of 20 square yards of carpeting priced at $18.00 per square yard.

12. What is $33\frac{1}{3}$% of $42.00?

13. At 2:00 p.m. the hands of a clock form an angle that measures how many degrees?

14. Multiply $(4 \times 10^3)(8 \times 10^{-8})$ and write the result in scientific notation.

Solve and check. Show all steps.

15. $0.6m + 1.5 = 4.8$

16. $\dfrac{2}{3}x - 6 = 18$

Add, subtract, multiply, or divide, as indicated:

17. $3^3 - \sqrt{49} + 5 \cdot 2^4$

18. 3 yd 2 ft 9 in. + 8 in.

19. $2.7\left(1\frac{2}{3} \div 3\right)$ (fraction)

20. $\dfrac{-5(-4) - 3(-2)(-1)}{(-2)}$

Math 87 by Hake & Saxon

1. Jorge's average score on the first 3 tests was 84. His average score on the next 5 tests was 88. What was his average score on all 8 tests?

2. Use a ratio box to solve this problem. After working 6 months, Gina received a raise of 25%. If her previous pay was $6.40 per hour, what was her hourly pay after the raise?

3. Write an equation to solve this problem. Sixty-five is what percent of 50?

4. Use two unit multipliers to convert 2.4 m² to cm².

5. Draw a diagram of this statement. Then answer the questions that follow.
    Three eggs were cracked. This was $\frac{1}{6}$ of the total number of eggs in the carton.
    (a) How many eggs were in the carton?
    (b) What percent of the eggs in the carton were not cracked?

6. Evaluate: $\dfrac{a + b}{c}$ if $a = -8$, $b = -6$, and $c = -2$

7. The perimeter of a certain square is 24 inches. Find the area of the square in square inches.

8. What is the probability of this spinner
    (a) stopping on an even number?
    (b) stopping on an odd number?

9. Find the volume of this triangular prism. Dimensions are in centimeters.

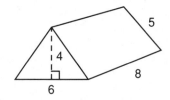

10. Find the area of this circle.

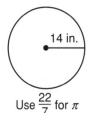

Use $\frac{22}{7}$ for π

11. Find the total price, including 7% tax, of 20 square yards of carpeting priced at $16.00 per square yard.

12. What is $33\frac{1}{3}\%$ of $48.00?

13. What is the measure of the angle formed by the hands of a clock at 4:00 a.m.?

14. Multiply $(3 \times 10^4)(7 \times 10^{-9})$ and write the result in scientific notation.

Solve and check. Show all steps.

15. $0.6m - 1.5 = 4.8$

16. $\dfrac{2}{3}x + 6 = 18$

Add, subtract, multiply, or divide, as indicated:

17. $3^3 - \sqrt{64} + 4 \cdot 2^4$

18. 2 yd 2 ft 7 in. + 8 in.

19. $4.5\left(3 \div 1\dfrac{2}{3}\right)$ (fraction)

20. $\dfrac{-5(-4) + 3(-2)(-1)}{(-2)}$

Math 87 by Hake & Saxon

1.   The dinner bill totaled $24.00. Daniel left a 15% tip. How much money did Daniel leave for a tip?

2.   The 200-kilometer drive took $2\frac{1}{2}$ hours. What was the average speed of the drive in kilometers per hour?

Use a ratio box to solve Problems 3 to 5.

3.   The $\frac{1}{12}$ scale model of the rocket stood 48 inches high. What was the height of the actual rocket?

4.   Sam saved $35 buying the suit at a 20% off sale. What was the regular price of the suit?

5.   A merchant bought an item for $30.00 and sold it for 50% more. For what price did the merchant sell the item?

6.   What is 6.5% of $48.00? Write an equation and solve it.

7.   (a) What are the coordinates of the fourth vertex of a rectangle whose other vertices are (4, 3), (−2, 3), and (−2, −1)?

     (b) What is the area of the rectangle?

8.   Use the Pythagorean theorem to find a. Dimensions are in inches.

Find the volume of the solids shown in Problems 9 and 10. Dimensions are in centimeters.

9.

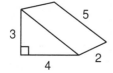

10.

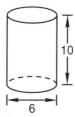

Use 3.14 for π

11. These two triangles are similar. Find x.

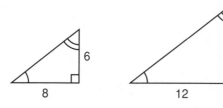

12. In this figure, find the measure of $\angle BOC$.

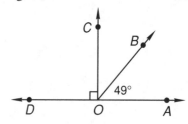

13. Arrange in order from least to greatest:

$$3, \; 3^2, \; \sqrt{3}, \; -3$$

14. Find the area of a circle whose radius is 6 inches. Use 3.14 for π.

15. Which of these numbers is between 7 and 9?

     A. $\sqrt{8}$ B. $\sqrt{79}$ C. $\sqrt{97}$

Solve:

16. $2\frac{2}{3}x + 6 = 14$

17. $\dfrac{20}{w} = \dfrac{45}{3.6}$

Add, subtract, multiply, or divide, as indicated:

18. $10.5\left(3 - 1\frac{4}{7}\right)$

19. $\sqrt{10^2 - 8^2}$

20. $\dfrac{(-18) - (-2)(-3)}{(-3) + (-2) - (-4)}$

Math 87 by Hake & Saxon

1. The dinner bill totaled $18.00. Daniel left a 15% tip. How much money did Daniel leave for a tip?

2. The 2100-mile flight took $3\frac{1}{2}$ hours. What was the average speed of the flight in miles per hour?

Use a ratio box to solve Problems 3 to 5.

3. The $\frac{1}{15}$ scale model rocket stood 30 inches high. What was the height of the actual rocket?

4. Sarah saved $15 buying the dress at a 20% off sale. What was the regular price of the dress?

5. A merchant bought an item for $50.00 and sold it for 30% more. For what price did the merchant sell the item?

6. What is 6.5% of $84.00? Write an equation and solve it.

7. (a) What are the coordinates of the fourth vertex of a rectangle whose other vertices are $(3, -2), (-1, -2)$, and $(-1, 2)$?

    (b) What is the area of the rectangle?

8. Use the Pythagorean theorem to find a. Dimensions are in inches.

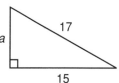

Find the volume of the solids shown in Problems 9 and 10. Dimensions are in centimeters.

9.

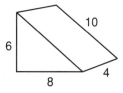

10.

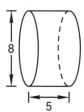

Use 3.14 for π

11. These two triangles are similar. Find x.

12. In this figure, find the measure of $\angle BOC$.

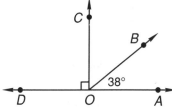

13. Arrange in order from least to greatest:

$$5, 5^2, \sqrt{5}, -5$$

14. Find the area of a circle whose radius is 7 inches. Use $\frac{22}{7}$ for π.

15. Which of these numbers is between 5 and 7?

    A. $\sqrt{6}$ B. $\sqrt{53}$ C. $\sqrt{35}$

Solve:

16. $2\frac{2}{3}x - 5 = 11$

17. $\frac{30}{w} = \frac{45}{3.6}$

Add, subtract, multiply, or divide, as indicated:

18. $5.25\left(3 - 1\frac{6}{7}\right)$

19. $\sqrt{10^2 - 6^2}$

20. $\dfrac{(-16) + (-2)(-3)}{(-3) + (-2)}$

Math 87 by Hake & Saxon

1. Find the (a) mean, (b) median, (c) mode, and (d) range for the following scores:

   88, 92, 89, 95, 88, 90, 89, 88, 87, 84

2. One card is drawn from a normal deck of 52 cards. What is the probability of drawing a red 5?

Use a ratio box to solve Problems 3 to 5.

3. Marla can exchange $200 for 300 Swiss francs. At that rate, how many dollars would a 210 franc Swiss watch cost?

4. The bag was filled with red marbles and blue marbles in the ratio of 5 to 7. If there were 180 marbles in the bag, how many were red?

5. During the off-season, the room rates at the resort were reduced 35%. If the usual rate was $120 per day, what was the off-season rate?

Write an equation to solve Problems 6 and 7.

6. What is 7.5% of $80.00?

7. Ten percent of what number is 350?

8. What is the area of the shaded region of this rectangle?

9. Use the formula $t = 1.06p$ to find t when p is 8.5.

10. Make a table that shows 3 pairs of numbers for the function $y = 2x - 1$. Then graph these pairs on the coordinate plane and draw a line through these points.

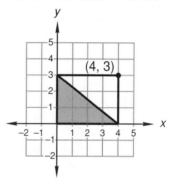

11. Find the perimeter of this figure. Dimensions are in centimeters. Use 3.14 for π.

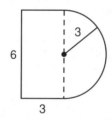

12. Find the volume of this right circular cylinder. Dimensions are in centimeters.

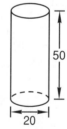

Use 3.14 for π

13. What is the surface area of a cube whose sides are 3 inches long?

14. Find $m\angle x$ in this figure.

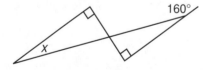

15. The triangles are similar. Find y.

Solve and check. Show all steps.

16. $1\frac{2}{3}x - 15 = 45$

17. $\dfrac{m}{35} = \dfrac{1.6}{14}$

Add, subtract, multiply, or divide, as indicated:

18. $100 - \{80 - 3[2 + 2(3^2)]\}$

19. $3\frac{3}{4} + 1\frac{1}{4} \cdot 8$

20. $\dfrac{(-6) - (7)(-4) - 1}{(-1) + (-2)}$

Math 87 by Hake & Saxon

1. Find the (a) mean, (b) median, (c) mode, and (d) range for the following scores:
    $$93, 97, 93, 100, 94, 93, 92, 90$$

2. One card is drawn from a normal deck of 52 cards. What is the probability of drawing an ace or a king?

Use a ratio box to solve Problems 3 to 5.

3. Hans can exchange $200 for 300 Swiss francs. At that rate, how many dollars would a 960 franc clock cost?

4. The jar was filled with peanuts and cashews in the ratio of 11 to 4. If the total number of peanuts and cashews in the jar was 630, how many peanuts were there?

5. During the off-season, the room rates at the resort were reduced 35%. If the usual rate was $140 per day, what was the off-season rate?

Write an equation to solve Problems 6 and 7.

6. What is 6.8% of $50.00?

7. Twenty percent of what number is 350?

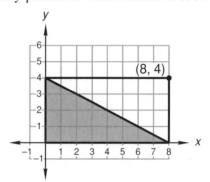

8. What is the area of the shaded region of this rectangle?

9. Use the formula $c = 2.54n$ to find c when n is 4.

10. Make a table that shows 3 pairs of numbers for the function $y = 2x + 1$. Then graph these pairs on the coordinate plane and draw a line through these points.

11. Find the perimeter of this figure. Dimensions are in centimeters. Use 3.14 for π.

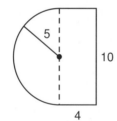

12. Find the volume of this right circular cylinder. Dimensions are in centimeters.

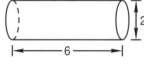

Use 3.14 for π

13. What is the surface area of a cube whose sides are 2 inches long?

14. Find $m\angle x$ in this figure.

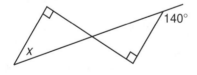

15. These triangles are similar. Find y.

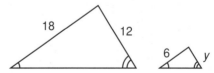

Solve and check. Show all steps.

16. $1\frac{2}{3}x + 15 = 45$

17. $\dfrac{w}{35} = \dfrac{1.5}{21}$

Add, subtract, multiply, or divide, as indicated:

18. $100 - \{90 - 3[4 + 3(2^3)]\}$

19. $1\frac{2}{3} + 3\frac{1}{3} \cdot 6$

20. $\dfrac{(-6) + (7)(-4) - 1}{(-1) - (-2)}$

Math 87 by Hake & Saxon

Use a ratio box to solve Problems 1 to 3.

1.   The regular price was $21.00, but the item was on sale for 30% off. What was the sale price?

2.   If 24 kilograms of seed cost $37, how much would 42 kilograms cost at the same rate?

3.   An item was on sale for 30% off the regular price. If the sale price was $21.00, what was the regular price?

4.   Ten billion is how much greater than nine hundred million? Write the answer in scientific notation.

5.   The median of these numbers is how much less than the mean?

1.5, 0.6, 0.7, 0.85, 5.3

6.   What is the probability of having a coin turn up heads on three consecutive tosses?

7.   What percent of $30 is $4.50? Write an equation.

8.   Tim left $3000 in an account that paid 8% simple interest annually. How much interest was earned in 2 years?

9.   The points (0, 3), (−3, 1), and (3, 1) are the vertices of a triangle. Find the area of the triangle.

10. Use two unit multipliers to convert 4 ft² to square inches.

11. If Jan walks from point A to point B to point C she walks 140 yards. How many yards would she save by taking the shortcut from point A to point C?

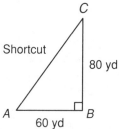

12. Find the volume of this pyramid. The square base is 30 m by 30 m. The height is 20 m.

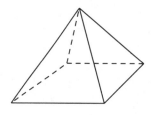

13. Make a table that shows 3 pairs of numbers for the function $y = -x + 2$. Then graph the number pairs on a coordinate plane and draw a line through the points to show other number pairs of the function.

14. Use the formula $A = \frac{1}{2}bh$ to find h when $A = 20$ and $b = 10$.

15. Find $m\angle x$.

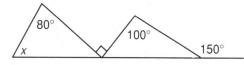

Solve and check. Show all steps.

16. $1\frac{3}{5}w - 17 = 23$

17. $\frac{7.5}{a} = \frac{25}{20}$

Add, subtract, multiply, or divide, as indicated:

18. 1.5 km − 860 m = _____ m

19. $2\frac{2}{3} + \left(2\frac{1}{2} \div 6\right)$

20. $\dfrac{(-7) - (-3) + (2)(-3)}{(-3) - (2)}$

Use a ratio box to solve Problems 1 to 3.

1. The regular price was $21.00, but the item was on sale for 25% off. What was the sale price?

2. If 24 pounds of seed cost $41.00, how much would 42 pounds cost at the same rate?

3. An item was on sale for 25% off the regular price. If the sale price was $21.00, what was the regular price?

4. Ten billion is how much greater than eight hundred million? Write the answer in scientific notation.

5. The median of these numbers is how much less than the mean?

   2.0, 0.6, 0.7, 0.85, 5.3

6. What is the probability of having a coin turn up heads, heads, tails, tails on 4 consecutive tosses?

7. What percent of $30 is $7.50? Write an equation.

8. Minh left $4000 in an account that paid 7% simple interest annually. How much interest was earned in 2 years?

9. The points (3, 0), (3, −4), and (0, −4) are the vertices of a triangle. Find the area of the triangle.

10. Use two unit multipliers to convert 6 yd^2 to square feet.

11. If Jan walks from point A to point B to point C she walks 35 yards. How many yards would she save by taking the shortcut from point A to point C?

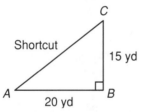

12. Find the volume of the cone. The diameter of the base is 20 inches and the height is 15 inches. Use 3.14 for π.

13. Make a table that shows 3 pairs of numbers for the function $y = -x - 1$. Then graph the number pairs on a coordinate plane and draw a line through the points to show other number pairs of the function.

14. Use the formula $A = \dfrac{1}{2}bh$ to find h when $A = 20$ and $b = 5$.

15. Find $m\angle x$.

Solve and check. Show all steps.

16. $2\dfrac{2}{3}y + 13 = 37$

17. $\dfrac{2.5}{a} = \dfrac{15}{21}$

Add, subtract, multiply, or divide, as indicated:

18. $1.5 \text{ km} - 720 \text{ m} =$ ____ m

19. $2\dfrac{2}{3} + \left(6 \div 2\dfrac{1}{2}\right)$

20. $\dfrac{(-7) + (-3) + (-2)(-3)}{(-3) - (-2)}$

Math 87 by Hake & Saxon

Math 87
Test Masters

Optional Quiz Forms

Instructions

Daily quizzes are an optional component of the Saxon program. Some teachers call these exercises "bellringers" or "warm-up activities." The purpose of these exercises is to get students "on task" as soon as they enter the classroom. Teachers can also use these quizzes to help alert themselves to potential problems which students may be having. Typically, a teacher places these problems on the chalkboard or on an overhead projector before the students enter the classroom. While the teacher is taking attendance, students work on these problems. The teacher need not grade each quiz individually. Some teachers review the exercises orally while other teachers randomly select students to provide solutions, either orally or at the chalkboard. **This whole process should take no more than 5 minutes.**

MATH 87 QUIZ 1

1. When the sum of 4 and 5 is subtracted from the product of 4 and 5, what is the difference?

2. $4.25 + 65¢ + $10 + 7¢

3. $\begin{array}{r} \$0.25 \\ \times \quad 14 \\ \hline \end{array}$

4. $\dfrac{648}{12}$

5. $316 - (45 - 8)$

MATH 87 QUIZ 2

1. When the product of 8 and 8 is divided by the sum of 8 and 8, what is the quotient?

2. $50 − ($6.45 + $3)

3.
$$\begin{array}{r} W \\ +\ 56 \\ \hline 87 \end{array}$$

4.
$$\begin{array}{r} Y \\ -\ 24 \\ \hline 37 \end{array}$$

5.
$$\begin{array}{r} Z \\ \times\ 8 \\ \hline 112 \end{array}$$

MATH 87 QUIZ 3

1. Arrange these numbers in order from least to greatest:

$$-3, 2, 0, -1$$

2. Replace the circle with the proper comparison symbol.

$$3 \cdot 3 \bigcirc 3 + 3$$

3.
$$\begin{array}{r} 56 \\ + A \\ \hline 124 \end{array}$$

4.
$$\begin{array}{r} 123 \\ - B \\ \hline 78 \end{array}$$

5.
$$\begin{array}{r} 21 \\ \times C \\ \hline 231 \end{array}$$

MATH 87 QUIZ 4

1. Show this subtraction problem on a number line: $2 - 5$

2. Replace each circle with the proper comparison symbol.

   (a) $-3 \bigcirc -5$ (b) $2 \cdot 6 \bigcirc 3(4)$

3. $\begin{array}{r} R \\ +\ 63 \\ \hline 360 \end{array}$

4. $\begin{array}{r} 300 \\ -\ \ S \\ \hline 115 \end{array}$

5. $\begin{array}{r} T \\ \times\ 15 \\ \hline 300 \end{array}$

MATH 87 QUIZ 5

1. Use words to write 37528400.

2. $10 – ($6.48 – 79¢)

3.
$$\begin{array}{r} 576 \\ +\;\;E \\ \hline 830 \end{array}$$

4.
$$\begin{array}{r} F \\ -\,263 \\ \hline 347 \end{array}$$

5.
$$\begin{array}{r} 36 \\ \times\;\;G \\ \hline 648 \end{array}$$

MATH 87 QUIZ 6

1. Use digits to write three hundred fifty million, thirty-five thousand, nine.

2. List the whole numbers that are factors of 21.

3. List the whole numbers from 1 to 10 that are divisors of 1410.

4.
$$\begin{array}{r} 567 \\ -\ G \\ \hline 279 \end{array}$$

5.
$$\begin{array}{r} 25 \\ \times\ H \\ \hline 600 \end{array}$$

MATH 87 QUIZ 7

1. Use words to write 5320105060.

2. List the whole numbers from 1 to 10 that are factors of 2160.

3. Name three segments in this figure.

$$Q \qquad R \qquad S$$

4.
$$\begin{array}{r} M \\ +\ 378 \\ \hline 783 \end{array}$$

5.
$$\begin{array}{r} N \\ -\ 520 \\ \hline 256 \end{array}$$

MATH 87 QUIZ 8

1. Use digits to write ten billion, six hundred million, fifty-three thousand.

2. List the whole numbers from 1 to 10 that are divisors of 3780.

3. Draw a circle and shade $\frac{2}{3}$ of it.

4. What is the name of the top number of a fraction?

5. Use digits and a comparison symbol to write "One and three fourths is less than two and one third."

MATH 87 QUIZ 9

1. Use words to write 30102050706.

2. (a) List the factors of 16.

   (b) List the factors of 24.

   (c) List the numbers that are factors of both 16 and 24.

3. Point A represents what mixed number on this number line?

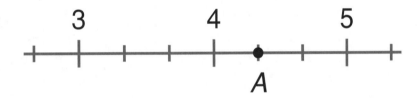

4. $\dfrac{3}{7} + \dfrac{2}{7}$

5. $\dfrac{3}{5} \times \dfrac{3}{4}$

MATH 87 QUIZ 10

1. Use digits to write ten billion, one hundred million, one thousand, one hundred ten.

2. Replace the circle with the proper comparison symbol.

$$\frac{1}{3} + \frac{1}{3} \bigcirc \frac{1}{3} \times \frac{1}{3}$$

3. List the single-digit numbers that are divisors of 450.

4. $\dfrac{5}{8} - \dfrac{5}{8}$

5. $\dfrac{1}{2} \cdot \dfrac{1}{2} \cdot \dfrac{1}{2}$

MATH 87 QUIZ 11

1. One thousand, two hundred runners began the race. Only 542 finished the race. How many runners dropped out along the way?

2. Arrange these numbers in order from least to greatest:

$$\frac{1}{3}, 1, 0, -3$$

3. Use words to write 1030040005.

4. $\dfrac{5}{8} + \dfrac{2}{8}$

5. $\dfrac{6}{7} \times \dfrac{3}{5}$

MATH 87 QUIZ 12

1. How many years were there from 1492 to 1601?

2. After spending $26.50 at the store, Dan had $8.90. How much money did Dan have when he went to the store?

3. Thirty-six thousand is how much less than one hundred thousand?

4. $\dfrac{5}{8} - \left(\dfrac{3}{8} + \dfrac{2}{8} \right)$

5. $\dfrac{1}{5} \cdot \dfrac{3}{4} \cdot \dfrac{3}{5}$

1. Movie tickets sold for $6 each. The total ticket sales were $930. How many tickets were sold?

2. Use digits to write one hundred ten billion, two hundred thousand.

3. What mixed number is represented by point *A* on this number line?

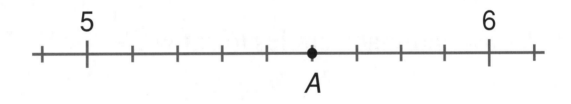

4. $\dfrac{5}{8} - \left(\dfrac{3}{8} - \dfrac{1}{8} \right)$

5. $(3 \cdot 6) \div (3 + 6)$

MATH 87 QUIZ 14

1. One fourth of the students earned an A on the test. What fraction of the students did not earn an A on the test?

2. Eighty-five thousand is how much more than nineteen thousand?

3. Draw and shade circles to show $2\frac{2}{3}$.

4. List the factors of 100.

5. $1000 \div (100 \div 10)$

MATH 87 QUIZ 15

1. Write a fraction equal to 1 that has 8 as the denominator.

2. Convert each improper fraction to either a whole number or a mixed number.

    (a) $\dfrac{8}{5}$ (b) $\dfrac{8}{4}$

3. Sixteen books could be packed in a box. Four thousand books needed to be packed. How many boxes could be filled?

4. Draw and shade circles to show that $1\dfrac{3}{4}$ equals $\dfrac{7}{4}$.

5. $\dfrac{7}{9} + \left(\dfrac{5}{9} - \dfrac{3}{9} \right)$

MATH 87 QUIZ 16

1. Find a fraction equivalent to $\frac{1}{2}$ that has a denominator of 10.

2. Three million is how much more than two hundred thirty thousand?

3. Arrange these numbers in order from least to greatest:

$$-1, \frac{2}{3}, 0, \frac{3}{2}, 1$$

4. Complete each equivalent fraction.

   (a) $\frac{2}{3} = \frac{?}{12}$ (b) $\frac{3}{4} = \frac{?}{12}$

5. Multiply $\frac{5}{3}$ and $\frac{2}{3}$ and write the product as a mixed number.

MATH 87 QUIZ 17

1. Two fifths of the lights were on. What fraction of the lights were off?

2. Reduce each fraction or mixed number to lowest terms.

   (a) $\dfrac{4}{12}$ (b) $4\dfrac{6}{9}$

3. For each fraction find an equivalent fraction that has a denominator of 12.

   (a) $\dfrac{5}{6}$ (b) $\dfrac{3}{4}$

4. $\dfrac{4}{5} + \dfrac{4}{5}$

5. $\dfrac{3}{5} \times \dfrac{2}{3}$

MATH 87 QUIZ 18

1. Reduce: $3\dfrac{8}{12}$

2. For each of these fractions find an equivalent fraction that has a denominator of 18.

   (a) $\dfrac{5}{6}$ (b) $\dfrac{5}{9}$

3. The number 640 is divisible by which single-digit numbers?

4. $\dfrac{5}{9} - \dfrac{2}{9}$

5. $\dfrac{3}{5} \times \dfrac{2}{3}$

MATH 87 QUIZ 19

1. Draw two perpendicular lines. What type of angles are formed by perpendicular lines?

2. Michael spends $\frac{3}{8}$ of his day at school. What fraction of his day is not spent at school?

3. Complete each equivalent fraction.

   (a) $\frac{3}{5} = \frac{?}{10}$ (b) $\frac{1}{2} = \frac{?}{10}$

4. $\frac{4}{5} + \frac{4}{5} + \frac{4}{5}$

5. $\frac{1}{2} \times \frac{2}{3} \cdot \frac{3}{4}$

MATH 87 QUIZ 20

1. One billion is how much greater than one million?

2. Draw segment AB perpendicular to segment BC. Then draw segment AC. What polygon is formed?

3. For each fraction find an equivalent fraction that has a denominator of 20.

   (a) $\dfrac{2}{5}$ (b) $\dfrac{3}{4}$

4. $\dfrac{3}{2} + \dfrac{3}{2}$

5. $\dfrac{3}{2} \cdot \dfrac{3}{2}$

MATH 87 QUIZ 21

1. If each side of a square is 6 inches long, what is its perimeter?

2. Find A and B.

   (a) $\dfrac{5}{6} = \dfrac{A}{30}$

   (b) $\dfrac{3}{10} = \dfrac{B}{30}$

3. What is the name of a polygon that has twice as many sides as a square?

4. $\dfrac{11}{12} - \dfrac{5}{12}$

5. $\dfrac{3}{5} \cdot \dfrac{5}{6} \cdot \dfrac{3}{4}$

1. The rectangular field was 300 feet long and 200 feet wide. What was the perimeter of the field?

2. Arrange these numbers in order from least to greatest:

$$\frac{1}{4}, -2, 1, \frac{1}{2}, 0$$

Solve each equation:

3. $5x = 70$

4. $26 + a = 42$

5. $y - 16 = 40$

1. Write the prime factorization of 72.

2. If the perimeter of a regular hexagon is 24 cm, what is the length of each of its sides?

3. Complete each equivalent fraction.

   (a) $\dfrac{5}{7} = \dfrac{?}{28}$

   (b) $\dfrac{3}{4} = \dfrac{?}{28}$

Solve:

4. $6x = 96$

5. $36 - x = 19$

Math 87   by Hake & Saxon

1. Write the prime factorization of 900.

2. The perimeter of this rectangle is 30 cm. What is the width of this rectangle?

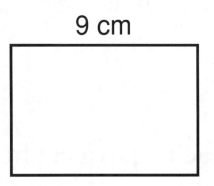

9 cm

3. $\dfrac{7}{8} + \dfrac{7}{8}$

Solve:

4. $109 = 19 + w$

5. $84 = 7m$

1. Write the prime factorization of 270.

2. This rectangle is twice as long as it is wide. What is its perimeter?

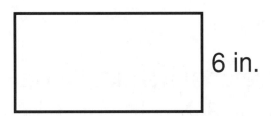

6 in.

3. Write each number as a fraction.

    (a) $3\dfrac{1}{2}$ (b) 3

4. Complete each equivalent fraction.

    (a) $\dfrac{5}{8} = \dfrac{?}{24}$ (b) $\dfrac{5}{12} = \dfrac{?}{24}$

5. $\dfrac{5}{6} - \left(\dfrac{1}{2} \cdot \dfrac{1}{3}\right)$

MATH 87 QUIZ 26

1. Three sevenths of the 28 students in the class were boys.

    (a) How many boys were in the class?

    (b) How many girls were in the class?

2. If the perimeter of a square is one yard, how many inches long is each side of the square?

3. Write each number as a fraction.

    (a) $5\dfrac{1}{4}$　　　　　　　　　(b) 5

4. $\dfrac{5}{6} + \left(\dfrac{1}{2} \cdot \dfrac{1}{3} \right)$

5. Solve:　$10n = 250$

MATH 87 QUIZ 27

1. Five ninths of the 36 pencils were broken.

    (a) How many pencils were broken?

    (b) How many pencils were not broken?

2. Sketch a rectangle that is 1 cm wide and 2 cm long. What is the perimeter of the rectangle?

3. $1\frac{2}{3} + 2\frac{2}{3}$

4. $4 - 1\frac{2}{5}$

5. Complete each equivalent fraction.

    (a) $\frac{5}{6} = \frac{?}{18}$ (b) $\frac{7}{9} = \frac{?}{18}$

Math 87 by Hake & Saxon

MATH 87 QUIZ 28

1. Write the prime factorization of 252.

2. What is the reciprocal of $2\frac{1}{2}$?

3. If the perimeter of a regular hexagon is one yard, how many inches long is each side of the hexagon?

4. $3\frac{5}{8} + 3\frac{5}{8}$

5. $5\frac{1}{6} - 1\frac{5}{6}$

MATH 87 QUIZ 29

1. Use prime factorization to reduce $\dfrac{196}{350}$.

2. Write the reciprocal of each number.

   (a) 4

   (b) $2\dfrac{3}{5}$

3. Reduce before multiplying:

$$\dfrac{5}{6} \cdot \dfrac{3}{4} \cdot \dfrac{8}{15}$$

4. $3\dfrac{3}{4} + 6\dfrac{3}{4}$

5. $5\dfrac{1}{8} - 3\dfrac{3}{8}$

MATH 87 QUIZ 30

1. Use prime factorization to reduce $\dfrac{375}{625}$.

2. Reduce before multiplying:

$$\frac{5}{8} \cdot \frac{3}{10} \cdot \frac{4}{9}$$

3. $3\dfrac{5}{8} + 1\dfrac{7}{8}$

4. $7 - 1\dfrac{3}{8}$

5. $\dfrac{3}{8} \div \dfrac{5}{6}$

MATH 87 QUIZ 31

1. Use prime factorization to reduce $\dfrac{135}{900}$.

2. $3\dfrac{1}{3} \times 2\dfrac{1}{2}$

3. $3\dfrac{1}{3} \div 2\dfrac{1}{2}$

4. $2\dfrac{5}{9} + 3\dfrac{7}{9}$

5. $9\dfrac{1}{6} - 4\dfrac{5}{6}$

MATH 87 QUIZ 32

1. Find the least common multiple (LCM) of 8 and 12.

2. $1\dfrac{1}{6} \times 3\dfrac{1}{3}$

3. $1\dfrac{1}{6} \div 3\dfrac{1}{3}$

4. $1\dfrac{5}{8} + 1\dfrac{5}{8}$

5. $8\dfrac{1}{8} - 7\dfrac{5}{8}$

MATH 87 QUIZ 33

1. Andrea went to the theater with $20.00 and bought three tickets. Then she had $8.75 left. What was the price of each ticket?

2. Find the least common multiple (LCM) of 9 and 12.

3. $3\frac{3}{8} \times 3$

4. $3\frac{3}{8} \div 3$

5. $3\frac{3}{8} + 3\frac{3}{8} + 3\frac{3}{8}$

MATH 87 QUIZ 34

1. What is the average of 42, 36, 57, 24, and 61?

2. Find the least common multiple of 4 and 8.

3. $2\dfrac{1}{2} \times 2\dfrac{2}{5}$

4. $2\dfrac{1}{2} \div 2\dfrac{2}{5}$

5. $5\dfrac{1}{9} - 3\dfrac{4}{9}$

Math 87 by Hake & Saxon

MATH 87 QUIZ 35

1. Round 1760 (a) to the nearest thousand and (b) to the nearest hundred.

2. What is the average of 432, 456, and 495?

3. $6 \times 4\frac{1}{2}$

4. $6 \div 4\frac{1}{2}$

5. $6 - 4\frac{1}{2}$

MATH 87 QUIZ 36

1. Round 3824 (a) to the nearest thousand and (b) to the nearest hundred.

2. $\dfrac{3}{4} + \dfrac{1}{8}$

3. $\dfrac{5}{6} - \dfrac{1}{4}$

4. $3\dfrac{1}{2} + 1\dfrac{1}{3}$

5. $4\dfrac{5}{6} - 1\dfrac{1}{2}$

MATH 87 QUIZ 37

1. Round 529 (a) to the nearest hundred and (b) to the nearest ten.

2. $3\dfrac{1}{3} + 1\dfrac{1}{6}$

3. $4\dfrac{3}{4} - 2\dfrac{2}{3}$

4. $1\dfrac{3}{5} \cdot 1\dfrac{1}{4}$

5. $8 \div 2\dfrac{2}{3}$

1. Use digits to write the decimal number twenty and five hundredths.

2. $3\frac{5}{6} + 1\frac{2}{3}$

3. $3\frac{5}{6} - 1\frac{1}{3}$

4. $5\frac{1}{3} \cdot 6$

5. $5\frac{1}{3} \div 6$

MATH 87 QUIZ 39

1. Round 14.2857 (a) to the nearest hundredth and (b) to the nearest whole number.

2. On her first 4 tests, Sarah scored 88, 88, 92, and 96. What was her average score on the first four tests?

3. $\dfrac{3}{4} + \dfrac{7}{8} + \dfrac{1}{2}$

4. $5\dfrac{1}{2} - 1\dfrac{5}{6}$

5. $3\dfrac{1}{5} \div 8$

MATH 87 QUIZ 40

1. Round 16.6666 (a) to the nearest tenth and (b) to the nearest whole number.

2. Find the number on the number line that is halfway between 1.2 and 1.3.

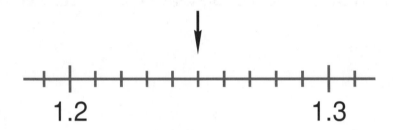

3. $2\frac{1}{2} + 3\frac{1}{3} + 4\frac{1}{6}$

4. $3 \cdot 3\frac{1}{3} \cdot 1\frac{1}{5}$

5. $5\frac{1}{8} - 1\frac{1}{2}$

MATH 87 QUIZ 41

1. Round one hundred twenty-seven thousandths to the nearest hundredth.

2. Find the number on the number line that is halfway between 12.5 and 12.6.

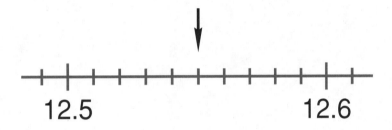

3. $3.4 + 2.85 + 5$

4. $4\dfrac{1}{3} - 1\dfrac{5}{6}$

5. $6\dfrac{2}{3} \div 2\dfrac{1}{7}$

MATH 87 QUIZ 42

1. In a class of 30 students there were 18 girls.

   (a) What was the boy-girl ratio?

   (b) What was the girl-boy ratio?

2. $5.6 + 12 + 0.58$

3. $4.7 - 2.563$

4. $3\frac{4}{5} + 2\frac{1}{2}$

5. $\frac{5}{6} \cdot 3 \cdot 2\frac{2}{5}$

1. The team won $\dfrac{3}{5}$ of the games they played and lost the rest. What was the team's won-lost ratio?

2. Find the perimeter of this figure. Dimensions are in centimeters.

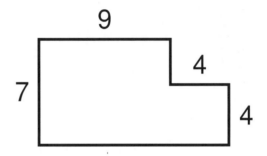

3. $12 - 5.46$

4. $8\dfrac{1}{3} - 1\dfrac{1}{2}$

5. $3\dfrac{3}{5} \div 3\dfrac{3}{10}$

Math 87 Quiz 44

1. The ratio of visitors to residents in the outback was 3 to 5. What fraction of the people in the outback were visitors?

2. Complete each equivalent fraction.

    (a) $\dfrac{?}{6} = \dfrac{16}{24}$ (b) $\dfrac{4}{7} = \dfrac{12}{?}$

3. $5.6 + 7.28 + 15$

4. $6\dfrac{2}{3} + 3\dfrac{3}{5}$

5. $2\dfrac{4}{5} \div 2\dfrac{1}{10}$

Math 87   by Hake & Saxon

MATH 87 QUIZ 45

Solve each proportion.

1. $\dfrac{M}{12} = \dfrac{2}{8}$

2. $\dfrac{30}{24} = \dfrac{20}{N}$

3. $10 - 0.028$

4. $4\dfrac{2}{5} - 1\dfrac{1}{2}$

5. $2\dfrac{2}{3} \cdot 6 \cdot \dfrac{5}{16}$

MATH 87 QUIZ 46

1. Solve the proportion: $\dfrac{W}{15} = \dfrac{15}{25}$

2. $(0.25)(0.03)$

3. $4.3 - (2 + 1.48)$

4. $7 \div 3\dfrac{1}{9}$

5. $\dfrac{1}{2} + \dfrac{3}{4} + \dfrac{7}{8}$

Math 87   by Hake & Saxon

MATH 87 QUIZ 47

1. Solve the proportion: $\dfrac{24}{R} = \dfrac{16}{12}$

2. 0.12×2.5

3. $0.144 \div 8$

4. $1\dfrac{1}{3} \cdot 1\dfrac{1}{5} \cdot 10$

5. $5\dfrac{1}{2} - \left(3 - 1\dfrac{1}{3}\right)$

Math 87 by Hake & Saxon

MATH 87 QUIZ 48

1. Divide 1.4 by 9 and write the quotient

    (a) with a bar over the repetend.

    (b) rounded to two decimal places.

2. Two sevenths of the boats in the harbor had sails. What fraction of the boats did not have sails?

3. Solve the proportion: $\dfrac{7}{x} = \dfrac{14}{4}$

4. (0.1)(0.2)(0.3)

5. $2\dfrac{1}{2} + 3\dfrac{1}{8} + 5\dfrac{1}{4}$

1. Write each of these numbers as a fraction or as a mixed number.

    (a) 0.125   (b) 25.04

2. Write each of these numbers as a decimal number.

    (a) $3\frac{3}{10}$ (b) $5\frac{1}{5}$

3. Round to the nearest thousandth: $0.\overline{7}$

4. $4 + \left(2\frac{1}{2} - 1\frac{1}{4}\right)$

5. $0.051 \div 3$

MATH 87 QUIZ 50

1. Divide 17 by 9 and write the answer

   (a) with a remainder.

   (b) as a decimal number.

2. The ratio of roses to petunias was 2 to 5. What fraction of the flowers were roses?

3. Write $2\frac{2}{3}$ as a decimal number.

4. $2\frac{1}{5} \cdot 5\frac{1}{3} \cdot 4$

5. $18.34 \div 4$

MATH 87 QUIZ 51

Divide:

1. $7.14 \div 0.3$

2. $8.26 \div 0.04$

3. Solve the proportion: $\dfrac{w}{15} = \dfrac{3}{5}$

4. The bobsled traveled 88 feet in 2 seconds. The bobsled averaged how many feet per second?

5. $\dfrac{3}{4} + \dfrac{3}{16} + \dfrac{5}{8}$

Math 87   by Hake & Saxon

MATH 87 QUIZ 52

1. What is the unit price of a 48-ounce box of soap that costs $5.76?

2. There were 24 hawkeyes and 16 jayhawks in the meadow. What was the ratio of hawkeyes to jayhawks?

3. Divide: $7.64 \div 0.05$

4. Write 5.05 as a mixed number.

5. 0.3×5.4

Math 87 by Hake & Saxon

MATH 87 QUIZ 53

1. Use words to show how each exponential expression is read.

   (a) 2^3 (b) 5^5

2. Simplify:

   (a) 2^5 (b) $2^4 - 3^2$

3. A 12-ounce bottle of car wash sells for $1.92. A 24-ounce bottle of car wash sells for $3.60. Which size is the better buy?

4. Divide 25 by 9 and write the answer with a bar over the repetend.

5. $0.025 + 1.237$

MATH 87 QUIZ 54

1. Write 649 in expanded notation by using powers of 10.

2. Multiply: 18.57×10^4

3. Round $72113.\overline{27}$ to the nearest

   (a) thousandth   (b) thousand

4. Write $5\dfrac{7}{8}$ as a decimal number.

5. $(0.07)(0.2)(0.04)$

MATH 87 QUIZ 55

Find the area of each rectangle.

1.

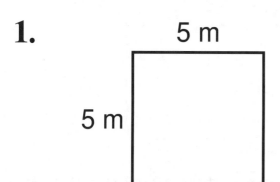

5 m

5 m

2.

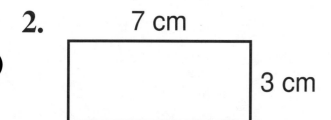

7 cm

3 cm

3. Write 3140 in expanded notation by using powers of 10.

4. If 5 pounds of apples cost $4.75, what is the price per pound?

5. $5.68 \div 0.04$

MATH 87 QUIZ 56

1. Simplify:

   (a) $\sqrt{144}$ (b) $\sqrt{25} + \sqrt{16}$

2. If the perimeter of a square is 32 cm, what is its area?

3. $8^2 - 3^3$

4. $1.7 \times 0.7 \times 7$

5. $2\frac{5}{6} + 3\frac{1}{12} + 4\frac{1}{4}$

MATH 87 QUIZ 57

1. Ashley drove 372 miles in 6 hours.

    (a) Write two rates for this statement.

    (b) What was her speed?

2. Sixteen ounces of syrup cost $2.88. What is the unit price?

3. If the perimeter of a square is 2 feet, its area is how many square inches?

4. $\sqrt{64} - \sqrt{25}$

5. $3.2 \times 2.3 \times 10^2$

MATH 87 QUIZ 58

1. Write each percent as a fraction or as a mixed number.

    (a) 15%   (b) 175%

2. Write each number as a percent.

    (a) $\dfrac{1}{20}$ (b) 3

3. Victor traded $35 for 945 francs. What was the rate of exchange in francs per dollar?

4. $2^3 + 1^5 + 4^2$

5. $\sqrt{49} + \sqrt{169}$

Math 87 Quiz 59

1. Change 73 inches to feet and inches.

2. Add: 3 yd 1 ft 7 in. + 2 yd 1 ft 5 in.

3. Write 320% as a mixed number.

4. $\sqrt{144} + 3^4$

5. 5.28×10^3

MATH 87 QUIZ 60

1. Leonard could fly 1200 miles in 4 hours.

    (a) Write two rates given by this statement.

    (b) How long would it take him to fly 1500 miles?

2. The perimeter of a rectangle is 22 cm. If the width of the rectangle is 5 cm, what is its area?

3.
$$
\begin{array}{r}
2 \text{ hr} \quad 31 \text{ min} \quad 23 \text{ sec} \\
+ \ 5 \text{ hr} \quad 29 \text{ min} \quad 36 \text{ sec} \\
\hline
\end{array}
$$

4. $11^2 + \sqrt{81}$

5. Write $\dfrac{3}{20}$ as a percent.

1. Find the area of this figure. Dimensions are in centimeters. All angles are right angles.

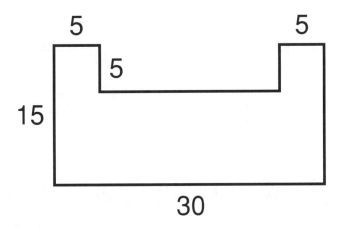

2. Rochelle could type 60 words per minute.

   (a) Write two rates given by this statement.

   (b) How many words could she type in 30 minutes?

3.   3 hr 25 min 15 sec
   + 5 hr 20 min 55 sec
   _____

4.   2 yd 1 ft 10 in.
   +   3 yd 3 ft   7 in.
   _____

5. $10^2 - \sqrt{25}$

MATH 87 QUIZ 62

1. Write each number in scientific notation.

   (a) 20,000

   (b) 4,500,000,000

2. Write each number in standard form.

   (a) 1.8×10^8

   (b) 2.4×10^6

3. Find the area of this figure. Dimensions are in meters. All angles are right angles.

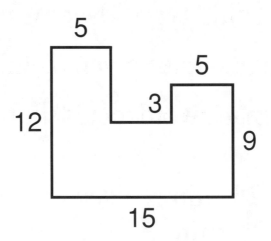

4.   5 days 12 hr 20 min
     + 4 days 15 hr 25 min
   ----

5. $3.25 \div 0.125$

MATH 87 QUIZ 63

Simplify:

1. $3 + 3 \cdot 3 - 3 \div 3$

2. $12 + 4 \cdot 3 - 24 + 2$

3. Write one billion in scientific notation.

4. Heather could swim 50 meters in 10 seconds.

   (a) Write two rates given by this statement.

   (b) How far could she swim in 25 seconds?

5. $0.25 \times 0.03 \times 10^4$

Math 87 Quiz 64

Use unit multipliers to perform the following conversions.

1. Convert 15 yards to feet. (3 ft = 1 yd)

2. Convert 25 meters to centimeters. (1 m = 100 cm)

3. Rachael's rocket is 3 yards tall. Bobby's rocket is 4 ft tall. Rachael's rocket is how many feet taller than Bobby's rocket?

4. $15 \div 3 + 4 \cdot 2 + 5$

5. $6 + 4 \div 4 - 3$

MATH 87 QUIZ 65

Use a ratio box to solve Problems 1 and 2.

1. The ratio of chipmunks to acorns in the forest was 2 to 8. If there were 200 acorns in the forest, how many chipmunks were there?

2. The ratio of sloops to catamarans in the bay was 2 to 5. If there were 35 catamarans in the bay, how many sloops were there?

3. The positive square root of 144 is how much less than 3 cubed?

4. Use a unit multiplier to convert 24 feet to yards.

5. $3.93 + 8.2 + 5$

MATH 87 QUIZ 66

1. The average of four numbers is 27. If three of the numbers are 25, 33, and 37, what is the fourth number?

2. After 4 tests, Marsha's average score was 89. If her score is 99 on the fifth test, what will be her average for all five tests?

3. Use a ratio box to solve this problem. The ratio of herbivores to carnivores in the zoo was 5 to 3. If there were 75 herbivores, how many carnivores were there?

4. Use a unit multiplier to convert 144 inches to feet.

5. $30 + 40 \div 8 - 7$

1.   4 yd 1 ft 6 in.
     − 3 yd 2 ft 7 in.
   _____

2.   4 days 5 hr 37 min
     − 2 days 7 hr 32 min
   _____

3. Use a ratio box to solve this problem. The ratio of ranchers to cattle is 2 to 150. If there are 900 cattle, how many ranchers are there?

4. The average of four numbers is 90. If three of the numbers are 82, 88, and 89, what is the fourth number?

5. $3\frac{1}{4} \cdot 2\frac{1}{2} \cdot 8$

MATH 87 QUIZ 68

Complete each unit conversion.

1. 1.3 L = _____ mL

2. 40 pt = _____ gal

3. If orange juice costs $0.15 per pint, what is the cost per gallon?

4.
$$\begin{array}{r} 3\text{ qt } 2\text{ pt } 4\text{ oz} \\ -\ 1\text{ qt } 2\text{ pt } 7\text{ oz} \\ \hline \end{array}$$

5. Use a ratio box to solve this problem. The ratio of photographs to paintings in the gallery was 2 to 9. If there were 72 paintings in the gallery, how many photographs were there?

MATH 87 QUIZ 69

1. Write each number in scientific notation.

   (a) 0.0000002   (b) 0.005

2. Write each number in standard form.

   (a) 7.3×10^{-6} (b) 4×10^{-4}

3. Use a unit multiplier to convert 8 pints to quarts.

4. $14 + (3.25 - 0.323)$

5. $13^2 - 12^2 + \sqrt{144}$

MATH 87 QUIZ 70

Answer true or false:

1. All squares are rectangles.

2. Some parallelograms are trapezoids.

3. Write 0.0000314 in scientific notation.

4. The field was planted with corn, beans, and wheat. If half was planted with corn and three eighths was planted with beans, what fraction of the field was planted with wheat?

5.
$$
\begin{array}{r}
5 \text{ wk} \\
- \ 2 \text{ wk} \ \ 4 \text{ days} \ \ 13 \text{ hr} \\
\hline
\end{array}
$$

Math 87   by Hake & Saxon

MATH 87 QUIZ 71

1. Find the perimeter and area of this parallelogram.
    Dimensions are in centimeters.

    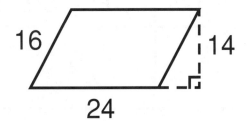

2. If quadrilateral *ACDF* is a rectangle and $\overline{BF} \parallel \overline{CE}$,
    classify each of the following quadrilaterals.

    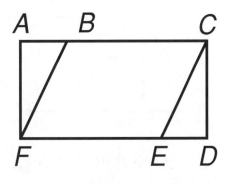

    (a) *AFDC*   (b) *CDFB*

3. Use a unit multiplier to convert 5280 feet to yards.

4.   5 gal 3 qt 1 pt 15 oz
     +   1 oz
    _____

5. $(3.4)(0.009)(10^2)$

1. Complete the table.

FRACTION	DECIMAL	PERCENT
(a)	0.15	(b)

2. Find the perimeter and area of this parallelogram. Dimensions are in centimeters.

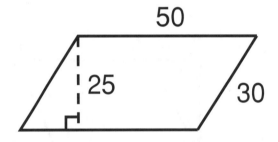

3. Use a ratio box to solve this problem. The ratio of gymnosperms to angiosperms in the forest was 9 to 4. If there were 1350 gymnosperms in the forest, how many angiosperms were there?

4. Which quantity is larger, a liter or a quart?

5.
$$
\begin{array}{r}
2 \text{ hr } \ 5 \text{ min } \ 35 \text{ sec} \\
- \quad 25 \text{ min } \ 17 \text{ sec} \\
\hline
\end{array}
$$

1. Find the next three numbers in this sequence.

$$8, \ 4, \ 2, \ 1, \ . \ . \ .$$

2. Find the missing number in this diagram.

```
 IN          F          OUT
             U
  2  →       N     →      4
             C
  7  →       T     →     49
             I
  5  →       O     →    [   ]
             N
  3  →             →      9
```

3. The Ogacihc Bucs won 5 of their 11 games but lost the rest.

   (a) What was the team's won-lost ratio?

   (b) What percent of the games did the team win?

4. Write 2.4×10^{-5} in standard form.

5. $(4.2)(3.14)(5^2)$

MATH 87 QUIZ 74

1. Sketch a number line to show this addition problem.

$$(+5) + (-3)$$

2. Find the next three numbers in this sequence.

$$-4, \ 0, \ 4, \ 8, \ . \ . \ .$$

3. Complete the table.

FRACTION	DECIMAL	PERCENT
(a)	(b)	35%

4. Gamma rays travel at approximately 3×10^8 meters per second. Write that number in standard form.

5. $\dfrac{2.5}{15} = \dfrac{x}{45}$

MATH 87 QUIZ 75

Write an equation to solve Problems 1 and 2.

1. What number is $\dfrac{3}{8}$ of 64?

2. Two fifths of 70 is what number?

3. Sketch a number line to show this addition problem.

$$(-3) \ + \ (+2)$$

4. Complete the table.

FRACTION	DECIMAL	PERCENT
$\dfrac{3}{8}$	(a)	(b)

5. Find the next three numbers in this sequence.

$$1, \ 4, \ 9, \ 16, \ . \ . \ .$$

MATH 87 QUIZ 76

Evaluate:

1. $ac - bc$ if $a = 5$, $b = 3$, and $c = 2$

2. $\dfrac{x}{6} - \dfrac{y}{6}$ if $x = 3$ and $y = 2$

3. Write an equation to solve this problem. What number is $\frac{2}{3}$ of 87?

4.   5 gal 3 qt 1 pt   2 oz
       − 2 gal 1 qt 1 pt 14 oz
       _____

5. 1 m − 25 cm = _____ cm

MATH 87 QUIZ 77

1. Classify each triangle by its angles.

   (a)    (b)

2. Classify each triangle by its sides.

   (a) 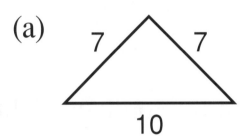   (b)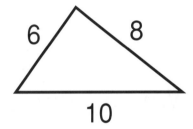

3. Write an equation to solve this problem. Five ninths of 81 is what number?

4. 1 L − 99 mL = _____ mL

5. $\dfrac{88\ \text{ft}}{\text{sec}} \cdot \dfrac{60\ \text{sec}}{1\ \text{min}}$

MATH 87 QUIZ 78

Simplify:

1. $100 - [50 - (30 - 5)]$

2. $\dfrac{3 + 4(1 + 4) + 2}{10 - 5(3 - 2)}$

3. Write an equation to solve this problem. Three fourths of 96 is what number?

Evaluate:

4. $ab - ac$ if $a = \dfrac{1}{2}$, $b = \dfrac{2}{3}$, and $c = \dfrac{1}{3}$

5. Divide 4.9 by 11 and write the answer with a bar over the repetend.

MATH 87 QUIZ 79

1. $(-27) + (-73)$

2. $75 - [15 + (50 - 15)]$

3. The product of x and 5 is 40. The product of y and 7 is 42. What is the product of x and y?

4. If we know that two sides of an isosceles triangle are 5 cm and 6 cm and that its perimeter is not 17 cm, then what is its perimeter?

5. Write an equation to solve this problem. What number is $\frac{4}{7}$ of 217?

Find the area of each triangle. Dimensions are in centimeters.

1.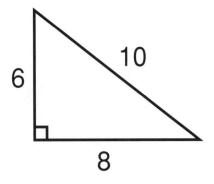

2.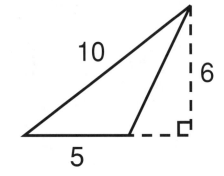

3. $(-54) + (+15) + (+64)$

Evaluate:

4. $ab - \dfrac{a}{b}$ if $a = 2$ and $b = 4$

5. $5\,\text{L} - 1760\,\text{mL} = \underline{\hspace{1cm}}\ \text{mL}$

MATH 87 QUIZ 81

Write an equation to solve Problems 1 and 2.

1. What number is 30 percent of 120?

2. Two percent of 50 is what number?

3. Use a ratio box to solve this problem. The ratio of nitrogen to phosphorous in the fertilizer was 2 to 1. If there were 16 pounds of nitrogen in the fertilizer, how many pounds of phosphorous were there?

4. $$\dfrac{4 + 5[2(30 - 20)]}{30 - (12 - 8)}$$

5. 2 m − 125 cm = _____ cm

MATH 87 QUIZ 82

Use a ratio box to solve Problems 1 and 2.

1. The ratio of toads to lily pads in the lake was 5 to 2. If there were 280 toads and lily pads altogether, how many lily pads were there?

2. The ratio of girls with curly hair to girls with straight hair was 7 to 3. If 35 girls had curly hair, how many girls were there in all?

3. Write an equation to solve this problem. What number is 20 percent of 45?

4. $3.4 \div (0.6 + 0.2)$

5. $\dfrac{x}{4} = \dfrac{27}{36}$

MATH 87 QUIZ 83

1. Use the name of a geometric solid to describe each shape.

   (a)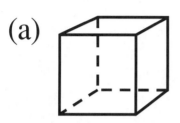

   (b)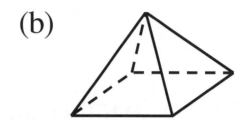

2. A pyramid has how many (a) faces and (b) edges?

3. Use a ratio box to solve this problem. The ratio of red apples to green apples was 5 to 3. If there were 72 apples in all, how many red apples were there?

4. Write an equation to solve this problem. What number is 12 percent of 50?

5. $\dfrac{3 + 5(4 - 3)}{3 + (8 - 7)}$

Math 87   by Hake & Saxon

MATH 87 QUIZ 84

Use a unit multiplier to perform each conversion.

1. 3 pounds to ounces

2. 50 grams to milligrams

3. A triangular prism has how many (a) edges and (b) vertices?

4. Use a ratio box to solve this problem. The ratio of supervisors to laborers at the job site was 2 to 7. Of the 171 individuals at the job site, how many were laborers?

5. $\dfrac{20 - 2[2 + (4 \cdot 3 - 10)]}{5 \cdot 3 - 7 \cdot 2}$

MATH 87 QUIZ 85

1. If the radius of a circle is 4 meters, its diameter is how many centimeters?

2. If the diameter of a circle is 4 ft, its radius is how many inches?

3. Use a unit multiplier to convert 144 ounces to pounds.

4.   5 lb 15 oz
     + 3 lb 14 oz
     _____

5.   7 gal 3 qt 1 pt 12 oz
     – 2 gal 2 qt 1 pt 14 oz
     _____

MATH 87 QUIZ 86

1. Find the circumference of each circle.

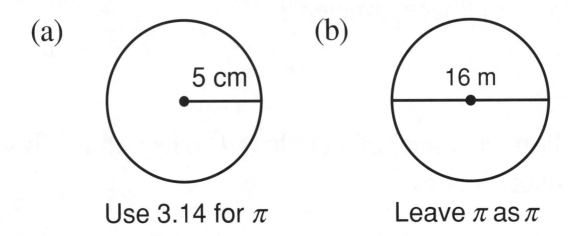

(a)

5 cm

Use 3.14 for π

(b)

16 m

Leave π as π

2. Use a unit multiplier to convert 5 pounds to ounces.

3. Write an equation to solve this problem. Thirty-four percent of 150 is what number?

4. $2 \text{ kg} - 450 \text{ g} = $ _____ g

5. $\dfrac{2 \cdot 2(5 - 2) + 3}{3 \cdot 2 - 1}$

MATH 87 QUIZ 87

Use algebraic addition to find these sums.

1. $(-7) - (+3)$

2. $(+2) - (-5) - (+3)$

3. Find the circumference of a circle whose radius is 7 cm.

4. Use a ratio box to solve this problem. The ratio of heartwood to sapwood in the old oak is 3 to 5. If there are 39 rings of heartwood, how many rings of sapwood are there?

5.   3 lb   3 oz
    − 1 lb 14 oz

MATH 87 QUIZ 88

Simplify each problem to the form indicated.

1. $3.25 - 1\frac{1}{8}$ (fraction)

2. $5.7 + \frac{5}{8}$ (decimal)

3. Use algebraic addition to find this sum.

$$(-3) - (-7) + (-4)$$

4. The diameter of the wagon wheel is 5 feet. What is the circumference of the wheel to the nearest foot?

5. Write an equation to solve this problem. What number is 0.28 of 75?

MATH 87 QUIZ 89

Use the addition rule to solve Problems 1 and 2.

1. $x + 73 = 592$

2. $m + 27 = 81$

3. $3\dfrac{3}{4} + 2.875$ (fraction)

4. Use a ratio box to solve this problem. The ratio of singers to dancers at the auditorium was 3 to 4. If there were 91 performers in all, how many dancers were there?

5. The radius of the circular stadium is 300 meters. What is the circumference of the stadium?

Math 87   by Hake & Saxon

MATH 87 QUIZ 90

1. Write each number in scientific notation.

(a) 34×10^6 (b) 0.27×10^{-4}

2. Use the addition rule to solve this problem.

$$x + 114 = 187$$

3. Use a unit multiplier to convert 72 inches to yards.

4. $3\dfrac{1}{5} + 0.35$ (fraction)

5.   5 yd 2 ft 11 in.
        + 2 yd 1 ft 10 in.
        _____

MATH 87 QUIZ 91

1. $3m = 72$

2. $\dfrac{5}{4}x = \dfrac{3}{4}$

3. Write 0.43×10^8 in scientific notation.

4. Use the addition rule to solve this problem.

$$y + 74 = 118$$

5. $\dfrac{5280 \text{ ft}}{\text{min}} \cdot \dfrac{1 \text{ mi}}{5280 \text{ ft}} \cdot \dfrac{60 \text{ min}}{\text{hr}}$

Math 87 by Hake & Saxon

MATH 87 QUIZ 92

1. What is the volume of this rectangular prism? Dimensions are in centimeters.

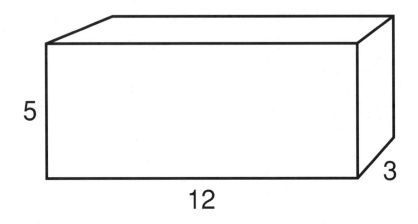

2. $0.08\,x = 1.52$

3. Write each of these numbers in scientific notation.

   (a) 50×10^{-7} (b) 0.18×10^{-12}

4. Use a unit multiplier to convert 3.5 liters to milliliters.

5. $(-3) - (-10) + (+5)$

MATH 87 QUIZ 93

1. Five eighths of the stars were on the main sequence. If 2240 stars were on the main sequence, how many stars were there in all?

2. Find the number of 1-cm cubes that can be placed in this box. Dimensions are in centimeters.

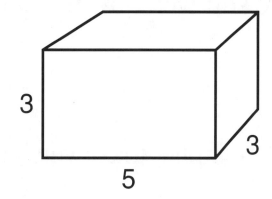

3. Write 0.57×10^{-5} in scientific notation.

4. What is the circumference of a tree whose radius is 10 inches.

5. $0.12\,x = 1.56$

Math 87 Quiz 94

1. Kyle can run 4 laps in 5 minutes. At that rate, how long will it take him to run 16 laps? Use the rate method to solve this problem.

2. Three sevenths of the bales were still wet. If 84 bales were still wet, how many bales were dry?

3. Use a unit multiplier to convert 7 pounds to ounces.

4.
$$
\begin{array}{r}
3 \text{ gal} \ 2 \text{ qt} \ 1 \text{ pt} \\
- \ 1 \text{ gal} \ 3 \text{ qt} \\
\hline
\end{array}
$$

5. $(-4) - (+5) - (-10)$

MATH 87 QUIZ 95

Write equations to solve Problems 1 and 2.

1. Seven eighths of what number is 161?

2. Twenty-seven is what decimal part of 180?

3. Use the rate method to solve this problem. Steve mowed 2 lawns in 5 hours. At that rate, how long would it take him to mow 6 lawns?

4. Write eighteen millionths in scientific notation.

5. $\dfrac{2 \ + \ 3(5 \ - \ 3) \ + \ 4}{8 \ - \ (4 \ - \ 2)}$

Math 87   by Hake & Saxon

Divide or multiply:

1. $(-6)(5)$

2. $\dfrac{-36}{-9}$

3. Write an equation to solve this problem. Two thirds of what number is 72?

4. Use a ratio box to solve this problem. The ratio of flowers to shrubs was 5 to 3. If there were 20 flowers, how many shrubs were there?

5. Write 500×10^{-5} in scientific notation.

MATH 87 QUIZ 97

1. Find the area of this figure. Dimensions are in centimeters. Corners that look square are square.

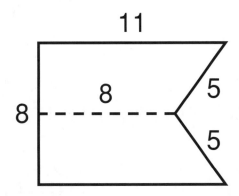

2. Write an equation to solve this problem. Eighty-one is what fraction of 243?

3.   4 hr 51 min 28 sec
  + 2 hr 21 min 31 sec
  _____

4. $(-12)(-11)$

5. $\dfrac{45}{-3}$

MATH 87 QUIZ 98

1. Simplify:

   (a) $\dfrac{\dfrac{12}{3}}{\dfrac{3}{8}}$

   (b) $\dfrac{12\dfrac{1}{2}}{100}$

2. Change each percent to a fraction.

   (a) $2\dfrac{7}{9}\%$

   (b) $83\dfrac{1}{3}\%$

3. Find the area of this figure. Dimensions are in centimeters. Corners that look square are square.

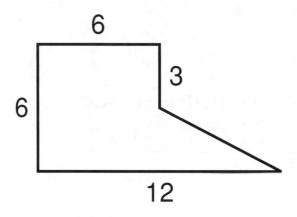

4. $(-56) + (-82) - (-47)$

5. $\dfrac{3(-5) - (-12)}{4 - 7}$

Math 87 Quiz 99

Write equations to solve Problems 1 and 2.

1. Eighteen is what percent of 72?

2. What percent of 84 is 14?

3. Change $5\frac{5}{9}\%$ to a fraction.

4. Simplify: $\dfrac{\frac{15}{3}}{5}$

5. Use a ratio box to solve this problem. The ratio of doctors to lawyers in the city was 7 to 4. If there were 260 lawyers in the city, how many doctors were there?

Math 87 Quiz 100

Graph each inequality on a number line.

1. $x > -3$

2. $x \leq 4$

3. Write an equation to solve this problem. What percent of 24 is 17?

4. Change $41\frac{2}{3}\%$ to a fraction.

5. Two thirds of the holes on the golf course contained water hazards. If 6 holes did not contain water hazards, how many holes were there in all?

1. Compare: $x \bigcirc y$ if $\dfrac{x}{y} < 0$

2. Compare: $x \bigcirc y$ if $x - y = 1$

3. Graph $x \geq 5$ on a number line.

4. Write an equation to solve this problem. Sixteen is what percent of 72?

5. $\dfrac{3 + 5(4 - 1) + 3}{3 + 2(5 - 3)}$

MATH 87 QUIZ 102

1.

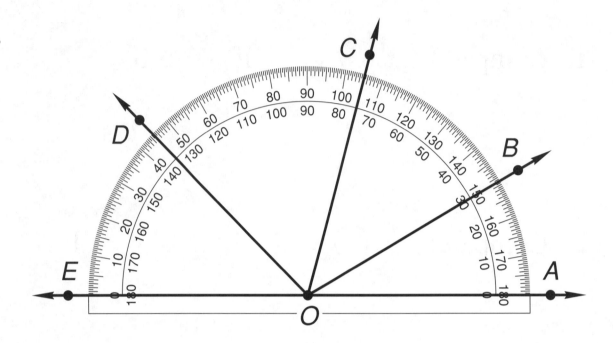

Find the measure of each angle.

(a) $\angle AOD$ (b) $\angle EOB$ (c) $\angle AOB$

2. Compare: $x \bigcirc y$ if x is negative and y is a whole number

3. Graph $x \le -2$ on a number line.

4. $\dfrac{4}{5}m = 20$

5. $3.14 = x + 1.32$

Math 87   **by Hake & Saxon**

Math 87 Quiz 103

Use a ratio box to solve Problems 1 and 2.

1. Twenty percent of the total income was used to pay the employees; the rest was used to purchase new machinery. If the total income was $150,000, how much was used to purchase new machinery?

2. Thirty-six of the 120 acres were planted in corn, and the rest was used as pasture. What percent of the 120 acres was used as pasture?

3. Graph $x > -2$ on a number line.

4. Write 0.65×10^5 in scientific notation.

5. (a) $(-4)(-4)$ (b) $\dfrac{16}{-4}$

1. Find the area of this circle. Use 3.14 for π.

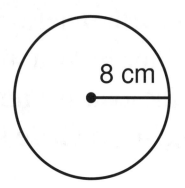

8 cm

2. Use a ratio box to solve this problem. Twenty percent of the 215 students answered the question correctly. How many students answered the question correctly?

3. Graph $x \leq -3$ on a number line.

4. Compare: $x \bigcirc y$ if $\dfrac{x}{y} = \dfrac{1}{2}$

5. $\dfrac{(-5)(-6)}{(-2)}$

MATH 87 QUIZ 105

1. Multiply and write each product in scientific notation.

   (a) $(5.3 \times 10^4)(8.4 \times 10^2)$

   (b) $(2 \times 10^{-7})(3.6 \times 10^{-4})$

2. Find the area of this circle. Use 3.14 for π.

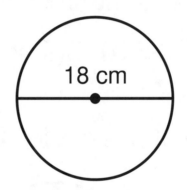

18 cm

3. Use a ratio box to solve this problem. Twenty-seven of the 90 boats had sails. What percent of the boats did not have sails?

4. Graph $x > -2$ on a number line.

5. $(-4) - (-5) + (-8)$

MATH 87 QUIZ 106

1. Rodney's scores on 8 tests were as follows:

    85, 92, 88, 88, 95, 90, 98, 100

    For this set of scores find the (a) mean, (b) median, (c) mode, and (d) range.

2. Multiply and write the product in scientific notation.

    $$(7 \times 10^{-5})(5 \times 10^{8})$$

3. Find the area of this circle. Use 3.14 for π.

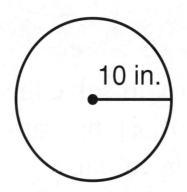

4. $\dfrac{(+5)(-4)}{(-2)(-5)}$

5. $(+40) - (-50) - (+30)$

MATH 87 QUIZ 107

1. Simplify: $(-4) + (-2)(-3) + \dfrac{(-10)}{(-2)}$

2. Find the missing numbers in this function.

$$y = 2x - 3$$

x	y
3	☐
☐	13
0	☐

3. Use a unit multiplier to convert 96 inches to feet.

4. Use a ratio box to solve this problem. If sound travels 3 miles in 15 seconds, how far does sound travel in 30 seconds?

5. Multiply and write the product in scientific notation.

$$(4.3 \times 10^7)(6 \times 10^{-5})$$

MATH 87 QUIZ 108

Answer true or false.

1. Every whole number is a counting number.

2. Every counting number is an integer.

3. Graph the whole numbers that are less than 5.

4. $(-4)[(-2) - (-3)(-4)]$

5. $3\{10 + [2^2 - 4(8 - 4)]\}$

MATH 87 QUIZ 109

1. For each fraction, write its corresponding percent.

    (a) $\dfrac{1}{3}$

    (b) $\dfrac{7}{8}$

2. For each percent, write its corresponding fraction.

    (a) 80%

    (b) $83\dfrac{1}{3}\%$

3. Graph the integers that are less than zero.

4. Use a ratio box to solve this problem. The sale price of $18 was 75 percent of the regular price. What was the regular price?

5. $\dfrac{(-4) + (-3)(-4)}{(-8) + (+4)}$

MATH 87 QUIZ 110

1. Use two unit multipliers to perform each conversion.

   (a) 20 ft² to in.²

   (b) $2\frac{1}{4}$ hr to seconds

2. Use a ratio box to solve this problem. The ratio of trumpets to flutes in the band was 5 to 3. If there were 24 flutes, how many trumpets were there?

Add, subtract, multiply, or divide, as indicated:

3. (a) $4\{3 \cdot 2 - 7[4 - (2 - 3)]\}$

   (b)   2 yd 2 ft 3 in.

      $-$ _____ 1 ft 8 in.
      _____

4. (a) $\dfrac{(-2)(-5) - (-4)}{(-4) - (+2)(+5)}$

   (b) $6\frac{1}{2} \div 12\frac{1}{2} \div 10^3$ (decimal)

5. Write an equation to solve this problem. What number is 35 percent of 7000?

1. Use this figure to find the measure of $\angle A$, $\angle B$, $\angle M$, and $\angle R$.

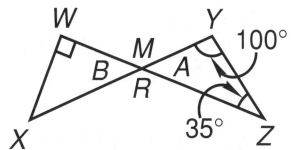

2. Use a ratio box to solve this problem. The ratio of cows to pigs on the farm was 5 to 3. If there were 20 cows, how many pigs were there?

3. Andrea bought the pants for $24. This was $\frac{4}{5}$ of the regular price.

   (a) What was the regular price of the pants?

   (b) Andrea bought the pants for what percent of the regular price?

4. Graph the integers less than -2.

5. Complete the table.

FRACTION	DECIMAL	PERCENT
$\frac{7}{12}$	(a)	(b)

MATH 87 QUIZ 112

1. Solve:

    (a) $4\frac{4}{5}x = 3\frac{3}{4}$ (b) $5\frac{1}{2}w = 440$

2. Forty-six is what percent of 50?

3. For this set of scores find the (a) mean, (b) median, (c) mode, and (d) range.

    5, 7, 3, 10, 6, 5, 4, 9, 7, 8, 10, 5

4. The product of 0.5 and 0.8 is how much less than the quotient of 0.5 and 0.8? Use words to write the answer.

5. What is the volume of a box with dimensions as shown? Dimensions are in inches.

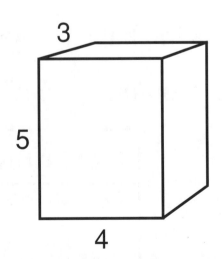

MATH 87 QUIZ 113

1. Evaluate each expression. Write parentheses as the first step.

   (a) $m + mr - r$ if $m = 2$ and $r = -5$

   (b) $-a + b - ab$ if $a = -3$ and $b = -2$

2. Simplify:

   (a) $-7 + 3 - 4 - 1$

   (b) $-1 + 4(-2) - 3(-1) + 4$

3. Use a ratio box to solve this problem. Sixty-six people came to the birthday party. This was 60 percent of those who were invited. How many were invited?

4. (a) Name this shape.

   (b) Find its perimeter.

   (c) Find its area.

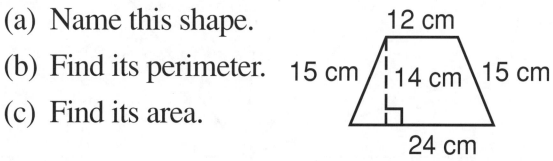

5. Multiply and write the product in scientific notation.

$$(3.6 \times 10^{-6})(8 \times 10^{-4})$$

1. Find the (a) sales tax and (b) the total price, including tax, of a $47.50 pair of shoes if the tax rate is 7 percent.

2. Find the total price, including 5 percent tax, for a $7.95 dinner, a $1.05 beverage, and a $3.20 dessert.

3. Compare: $a \bigcirc b$ if a is a whole number and b is an integer

4. How much money does Larry earn working for 5 hours 15 minutes at $7 per hour?

5.

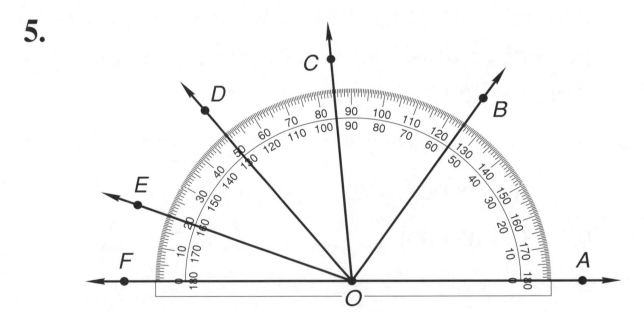

   (a) Find $m\angle AOD$.   (b) Find $m\angle FOE$.

   (c) Find $m\angle BOF$.   (d) Find $m\angle BOA$.

MATH 87 QUIZ 115

1. Write an equation to solve each problem.

   (a) What is 130 percent of 80?

   (b) Fifty-five is 220 percent of what number?

2. Use two unit multipliers to convert 270 ft² to square yards.

3. Complete the table.

FRACTION	DECIMAL	PERCENT
(a)	(b)	$37\frac{1}{2}\%$

4. Find the missing numbers in this function.

$$y = 4x - 1$$

x	y
3	☐
−2	☐
☐	19

5. Find the circumference of this circle.

14 m

Use $\frac{22}{7}$ for π

Math 87   by Hake & Saxon

MATH 87 QUIZ 116

Use a ratio box to solve Problems 1 and 2.

1. The regular price was $38.00, but the item was on sale for 25 percent off. What was the sale price?

2. The country's population increased 15 percent from 1980 to 1990. If the country's population in 1980 was 450,000, what was the country's population in 1990?

3. After 4 tests Dawn's average score was 85. What score must she average on the next 4 tests to have an 8-test average of 90?

4. Compare: 40% of 50 $\bigcirc$ 50% of 40

5. Add, subtract, multiply, or divide, as indicated:

(a) $(4 \cdot 2)^2 - 4(2^2) + 4^2$

(b) $1\,L - 325\,mL$

MATH 87 QUIZ 117

Solve:

1. (a) $4x - 3 = 9$

   (b) $\dfrac{4}{5}x + 2 = 6$

2. (a) $0.3x + 2.3 = 5$ (b) $2.4x - 0.4 = 4.4$

3. Seven twelfths of the 60 band students had brown hair.

   (a) How many students did not have brown hair?

   (b) What percent of the students had brown hair?

4. Find the total price, including 7 percent tax, for a $8.95 dinner, two 75¢ beverages, and a $1.55 dessert.

5. Each edge of the cube was $5\dfrac{1}{2}$ inches. What was the volume of the cube?

MATH 87 QUIZ 118

1. What is the probability of this spinner stopping on an even number?

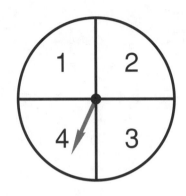

2. What is the probability of this spinner stopping on 4?

3. Use two unit multipliers to perform each conversion.

    (a) 5 weeks to hours   (b) 4 yd² to square feet

4. The length of each side of the square equals the diameter of the circle. The area of the circle is how much less than the area of the square?

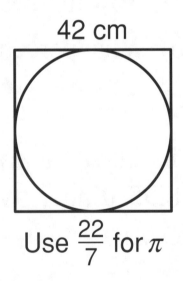

42 cm

Use $\frac{22}{7}$ for π

5. Solve:

    (a) $2\frac{1}{3}x + 4 = 11$ (b) $1.2x - 4 = 3.8$

MATH 87 QUIZ 119

For Problems 1 and 2, find the volume of each right solid shown. Dimensions are in centimeters.

1.

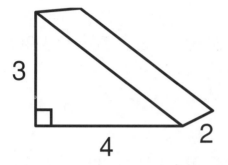

2.

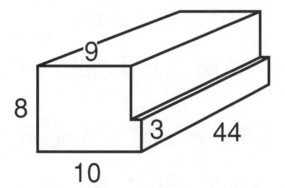

3. From Ken's house to school is 45 km. If he completed the round trip on his bike in 4 hours 30 minutes, what was his average speed in kilometers per hour?

4. What is 8 percent of $50?

5. Graph all the positive integers that are less than 3.

MATH 87 QUIZ 120

1. Graph the following points on a coordinate plane:

   (a) $(0, -2)$ (b) $(4, 3)$ (c) $(-2, -5)$

2. Multiply and write the product in scientific notation.

   $$(4.2 \times 10^5)(9.1 \times 10^{-7})$$

3. If a card is drawn from a normal deck of 52 cards (13 spades, 13 hearts, 13 diamonds, 13 clubs), what is the probability that the card is

   (a) a club?   (b) a red eight?

4. The radio cost $78. The tax rate is 8 percent.

   (a) What is the tax on the radio?

   (b) What is the total price, including tax?

5. Find the volume of this solid. Dimensions are in yards.

1. Use the clock face to estimate the measure of each angle.

(a) $\angle DOB$

(b) $\angle AOB$

(c) $\angle DOA$

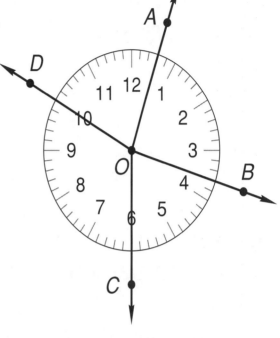

Compare:

2. $x - y \bigcirc y - x$ \qquad if $y < 0$

3. Use a ratio box to solve this problem. One hundred sixty-five is 40 percent less than what number?

4. Complete the table.

Fraction	Decimal	Percent
(a)	(b)	$8\frac{1}{3}\%$

5. The perimeter of a certain square is 2 yards. Find the area of the square in square inches.

MATH 87 QUIZ 122

1. The triangles are similar. Find x and y. Dimensions are in feet.

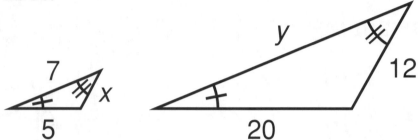

2. Write an equation to solve this problem. Seventy is what percent of 80?

3. Find (a) the circumference and (b) the area of a circle with a radius of 15 centimeters.

4. Four hundred twenty billion is how much less than seven trillion? Write the answer in scientific notation.

5. Refer to the figure shown. What are the measures of angles x, y, and z?

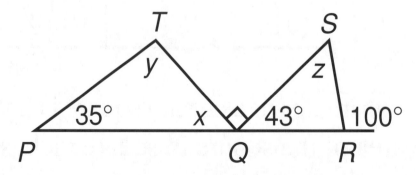

MATH 87 QUIZ 123

1. Use a ratio box to solve this problem. Jackie is molding a model of an elephant from clay on a scale of 1:24. If the elephant is 10 feet 6 inches tall, then the model should be how many inches tall?

2. Solve by using the scale factor.

   (a) $\dfrac{4}{9} = \dfrac{36}{w}$

   (b) $\dfrac{x}{8} = \dfrac{45}{120}$

3. Write an equation to solve each problem.

   (a) Three hundred thirty is what percent of two hundred twenty?

   (b) What is 70 percent of $21?

4. Graph a number line: $x \geq -5$

5. Add, subtract, multiply, or divide, as indicated:

$$\frac{(-4)(-2) \ - \ (-3)(4) \ + \ (-5)}{3(-2) \ - \ (-1)(-4) \ - \ (-5)}$$

MATH 87 QUIZ 124

1. Use the Pythagorean theorem to find side a.

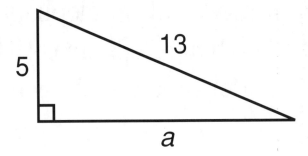

2. Use the Pythagorean theorem to find side c.

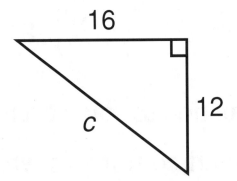

3. Use a ratio box to solve this problem. On a 1:24 scale model car, the length is 6 inches. The length of the actual car is how many feet?

4. $4^2 + 3^3 - \sqrt{256}$

5. $\dfrac{-10 - (5)(-4)}{8 + (-3)}$

MATH 87 QUIZ 125

1. Each square root is between which two consecutive whole numbers?

   (a) $\sqrt{50}$ (b) $\sqrt{75}$

2. Describe each pair of angles as complementary or supplementary.

   (a) 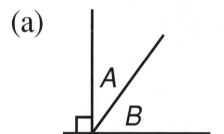   (b)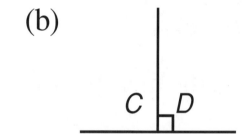

3. Use the Pythagorean theorem to find w.

   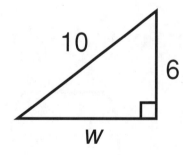

4. Solve by using the scale factor: $\dfrac{5}{8} = \dfrac{25}{x}$

5. Use unit multipliers to convert 21 yd² to square feet.

Simplify:

1. $(-8)(-5)(+2)(-3)(-1)$

2. $(-3)^5$

3. Each square root is between which two consecutive whole numbers?

(a) $\sqrt{125}$ (b) $\sqrt{88}$

4. Find the measure of $\angle P$.

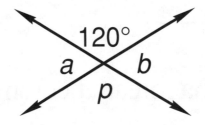

5. Find the volume of this right circular cylinder.

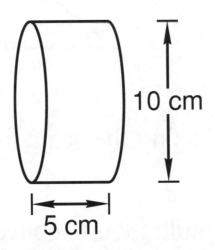

10 cm

5 cm

MATH 87 QUIZ 127

1. Find the perimeter of this figure. Dimensions are in inches.

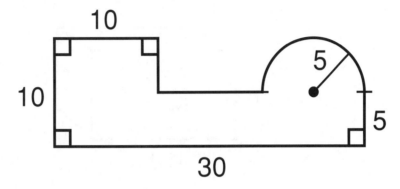

2. Find the area of the figure in Problem 1.

3. Find the measure of ∠*m*.

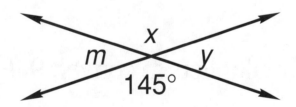

4. $(-2)^5 + (-3)^2$

5. $(-5)(-4)(+5)(+3)$

MATH 87 QUIZ 128

1. Find the surface area of this rectangular solid. Dimensions are in centimeters.

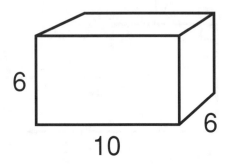

2. Find the area of this figure. Dimensions are in inches.

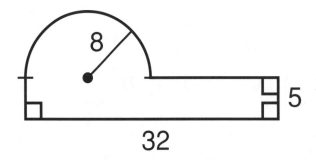

3. Use unit multipliers to convert 9 ft^2 to square yards.

4. $$\frac{(-5)(-8) \; - \; (5)(-4)(2)}{(-6) \; - \; (-2)}$$

5. Three fourths of a mile is how many yards?
   (1 mi = 1760 yd)

MATH 87 QUIZ 129

1. Solve for w: $w - y = x$

2. The formula for the area of a triangle is

$$A = \frac{1}{2}bh$$

Solve this equation for b.

3. Find the surface area of this right triangular prism. Dimensions are in centimeters.

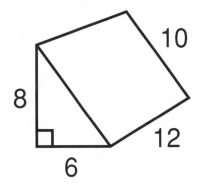

4. Multiply and write the product in scientific notation.

$$(3.4 \times 10^{-8})(4.5 \times 10^4)$$

5. $42 - [2^3 + 4(25 - 3^2)]$

Math 87   by Hake & Saxon

Math 87 Quiz 130

Make a table for each of these linear functions. Find three pairs of x and y for each function. Then plot the pairs and draw the graphs of the functions.

1. $y = 2x + 1$

2. $y = -x - 2$

3. Solve for x: $x + w = 2b$

4. Solve for a: $d = \dfrac{1}{2}at^2$

5. $36 - [4^2 - 5(-3)]$

MATH 87 QUIZ 131

1. Use the formula $A = \dfrac{1}{2}bh$ to find h when A is 36 and b is 12.

2. Use the formula $C = \dfrac{5}{9}(F - 32)$ to find C when F is 68.

3. Make a table that shows three pairs of numbers for the function $y = x + 2$. Then graph the number pairs on a coordinate plane and draw a line through the points.

4. Solve for y: $\quad y - b = mx$

5. $34 - [(+4)(-3) - (-2)(+3)]$

MATH 87 QUIZ 132

1. How much interest is earned in 5 years on a deposit of $1000 at 9 percent simple interest?

2. Brooks deposited $2000 in the bank at 8 percent simple interest for 2 years. How much money will he have in the bank after 2 years?

3. Use the formula $d = rt$ to solve for t when d is 36 and r is 4.

4. Find $m\angle x$.

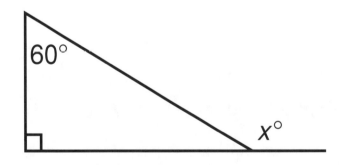

5. $(-2)^3 - (2)^3$

MATH 87 QUIZ 133

1. What is the probability of having a fair coin turn up heads, heads, tails on three consecutive tosses?

2. What is the probability of rolling a 2 and then a number less than 4 on two rolls of a single die?

3. Renae deposited $5000 in the bank at 7 percent simple interest. Three years later she withdrew the deposit and the interest she had earned. How much money did she withdraw?

4. What fraction of 96 is 8?

5. $\dfrac{18}{3.5} = \dfrac{54}{x}$

MATH 87 QUIZ 134

For Problems 1 and 2, find the volume of the figure shown. Dimensions are in centimeters.

1.

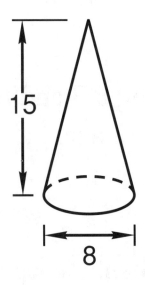

2.

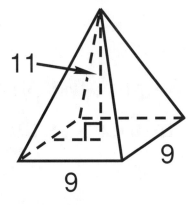

3. A card is drawn from a deck of 52 playing cards. The card was then replaced. Another card was drawn. What was the probability that the first card was a red king and the second card was a club?

4. $(-7) - (-5) - (+3) + (-1)$

5. $10^2 - [(-5)(-4) + (-3)(-10)]$

1. In a bag there are 5 blue marbles, 9 green marbles, and 10 red marbles. One marble is to be drawn from the bag.

   (a) What is the probability that the marble will be green?

   (b) What are the odds that the marble will not be blue?

2. A 40 percent chance of rain was forecast. What are the odds that it will rain?

3. Find the volume of this cone. Dimensions are in meters.

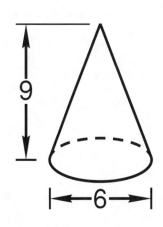

4. Solve for x: $y = mx + b$

5. $(-5) - (-12) + (-4)(-2)$

Show **all** work on this paper. Do not write on the test.

1.

2.

3.

4.

5.

6.

7.

8.

9.

10.

Show **all** work on this paper. Do not write on the test.

11.

12.

13.

14.

15.

16.

17.

18.

19.

20.

Name _____

Show **all** work on this paper. Do not write on the test.